ISHAN KAMDAR

To Sejal and Kush

PROLOGUE

I never excelled at English at school. Maths was my thing, not English, which is probably true for a lot of first generation Indians in the UK. Maths came more easily to our multi-lingual parents, and so was prioritised at an earlier age, and we got better at it. In fact until the age of 3 I had no English. My household, although based in London, was completely Gujarati. My first teacher hauled my parents in on my first day and got them to reset our home language as she had no way of communicating with me. From then on home was all English, but I never got any better at it. Obviously as a millennial, I blame my parents. I was laughed at by my teachers for long sentences, incoherent language and limited vocabulary, from grade school, all the way throughout university. I barely re-read my dissertation before submitting, to my own detriment.

Therefore it was never in my plan to write a book. This came to me in the middle of the night, whilst starved of live action sport in the middle of the coronavirus lockdown, and I couldn't stop thinking about it. Could it be possible to capture the suspense, thrill and imagination of sport, in the 21st century, while not experiencing it or watching it live?

I like nearly all sports. Watching that is. I play barely any. When it comes to watching sport I consider myself a jack-of-all trades fan. As long as it's live and I know the rules I will watch it. Football, Rugby, F1, Golf, Cricket, .. Darts .. whatever. They have even started to show the Indian Kabbadi league on UK tv now and I go a bit crazy when the Olympics comes around. I wouldn't say I was an expert in any of them, and so I couldn't tell you who the coach was when England won the Rugby world cup in 2003, I just remember they won, and Jonny Wilkinson won it in the last few minutes, and then danced around. I play golf, so I have a better knowledge of that, used to play cricket and was forced to play rugby for a term at school. Other than that, I am not particularly sporty myself. I like to tell myself that I prefer to watch the experts do it, and when they do it well there is no greater entertainment.

The sports I like are all completely made up, usually by the English or Scottish, and would be completely alien to foreign invaders. Boxing is easy to understand, but I'm not a big fan. I need complicated, convoluted rules which can only be passed down through the generations by watching or playing the sport. Knowing the complicated rules gives me the feeling of being in the know; that just by understanding all the rules and objectives of the game, you are in a special group of likeminded people, elevated above everyone else. These nuances and strategies bring so much entertainment, mystery, suspense and ultimately joy.

Cricket is exactly one of these sports. It's so complicated and laced with intrigue, strategy and strength that the majority of the world doesn't have a clue. Cricket will never be in the Olympics. It was created in the 1800s by some Englishmen and exported all over the world by the British Empire - and that is where it stuck. Today at a professional level cricket is only played by around 25 countries, and the "World Cup" is contested by 12 of them. There are 195 countries in total, I would remind you. That being said it is one of the biggest sports in the world, because of India. In the last 50 years cricket has come to dominate the sporting lives of over 1.2bn people in India. It is their escapism, their entertainment, in otherwise very difficult lives. Add that to the other countries that play cricket, and maybe with rounding you will get to 1.3bn people. The game is what has come to connect India and England, and has connected with the Indian diaspora around the world.

I was brought up on cricket. I played it at school, attended matches when I could especially at Lord's and have watched it ever since. As an overweight teenager, a twenty-something and now thirty-something, I didn't play it very well. I had good hand-eye coordination and a steady demeanour while batting and could rip it a bit when bowling. But I really couldn't run, and a top "career" score of 74* wasn't going to earn me many medals. I was solid 3rd XI material, meaning I was about good enough to make up the numbers in the third string.

But cricket is all about numbers and it is the maths I loved. I was able to fully score my father's Sunday league team by the time I was 9 with all the summary stats to go with it. He was better than me and had a regular place in his "lads" team batting at 3 or 4. Our weekends were pitched around his matches and it became our summer tradition to get all my homework done on Saturday, and spend Sunday at the cricket. Mum and the other "aunties" would make the teas and as long as the rain stayed away, which is rare in North London, everyone was out for a good time. So cricket became part of life, and my childhood.

So this is a tale about cricket. It captured my imagination when I was a child and continues to do so today. For an English cricket fan, the summer of 2019 was probably the cricketing highlight of our lives. For example; the extra time "Super Over" in the World Cup final and a last-wicket victory in an Ashes test which should have been lost are heart-stopping moments that only cricket and sport in general can give when you care so much about something that really has nothing to do with you.

I didn't see either of those events live, but followed them through all the media available to me at that time. I watched the final on TV, on twitter and the BBC sport live feed. I had a ticket to the game, but couldn't make it. Can you believe it! I "watched" the famous Ashes last wicket stand on BBC live feed with a very poor refresh rate while driving around Italy. Both were heart-in-mouth moments and with hindsight, it was the best cricketing summer ever. It was not only created by the action in front of us, although that is 80% of it, but the way it is viewed and the varieties of engagement that surround it. The commentaries, the stats, the updates, the interviews, the emotion, both on and off the field. Watching twitter while watching anything live is the only way to do it. For all its crudity the internet is a fantastic place, and as long as you only read the "liked" posts, the whole experience is enhanced. Twitter helps you confirm the rest of the world is thinking exactly what you are: Trent Boult stepping over the boundary rope when the game is on the line was a school boy error and cost them the match .. "how could he?".

It is this way of watching and this excitement that I want to capture, because in 2020, global circumstances have turned the sporting world off. We are all stuck at home, pleading for some watchable moment to restart. Reading twitter while watching Netflix isn't the same thing, and there is only so much COVID-19 misery and death that you can read about.

So why am I writing a book?

Firstly I suppose the question is "why a book?" I don't have a face for YouTube, or a voice for radio: and in an age where content creation is everything there are limited other choices so fiction is my chance. Most importantly it is for charity. The proceeds of the book will go to the Kamdar Foundation charity, which supports underprivileged children's education in the UK, India and East Africa. More details about the charity can be found at the back of the book. Thanks for supporting.

Secondly I want to be entertained myself as I am writing. This book is going to be different to others that you will have read. The secret: as I am writing the introduction now, I have no idea what the beginning, middle or end is going to look like. The story is not planned and will play out like live action. There is no excitement in knowing how it is going to end before it starts. That's not what sport is about. That's not what makes it special. So this new style of storytelling will be sport: live and direct.

It is unplanned because I will not know what is happening on the next ball as I each ball unfolds. Each ball will be independently generated as it happens, giving me some suspense and drama alongside you. We start at the top of the day, at the start of a One Day International, and finish with a result. The story plays out in the action of the match, with its twist and turns, and with a winner (or a very unlikely draw). Like all sport it could be a complete let-down, the story at least, if not the writing. The World Cup Cricket Final in 1999 was about as one-sided as you can get. Pakistan were all out for 145 and Adam Gilchrist knocked most of them off himself. But we still watched; for the story; for the commitment to sport; for the chance to see something special. If we get an interesting enough result then I may even write about the second ODI, so fingers crossed.

I am going to write it in a way that a millennial consumes information these days: twitter, Wikipedia, Cricinfo, TV, radio,

YouTube, podcasts all at the same time. Hopefully if you are a cricket-watching enthusiast you will be familiar with the commentary style. That being said for me stories and sport are all about the characters that are involved. Stokes' world cup redemption, or Smith's Ashes comeback, for example. Without the spice, would they have been so good? So all of the "prose" in this book is going to build that out. Let me say clearly these are completely fictional and have not been directly based on any past, present or future professional cricketers or people in the wider cricketing world. But let's be honest: there is a 'type.' Late 20s early 30s, public school, probably went to Cambridge, married, kid on the way, Mr Nice Guy? I could have been great if I had been any good.

So if you don't have a clue about cricket, this is not the book for you. Thanks for the purchase and the support but after this introduction things may get confusing. Terminology, cricketing knowledge and banter, etc. are to a certain extent assumed going past this point. My dissertation over 10 years ago was the last time I wrote anything longer than 1000 words and given that we have now gone close to 2000 words already I am going to give myself a pat on the back and get on with it.

THE GAMEPLAY, MATHS AND UNCERTAINTY

Maths, after a certain age, becomes more about the letters than numbers, and that is what I am going to use it for. As I mentioned, this story is unscripted, meaning that I don't yet know who is going to win. In order to generate the action and play out the game I will be using a version of Book Cricket. This will determine what happens on every ball of the match, how one ball or action affects or moves the script, and gives us live action and a result.

Here we assign a cricketing value to every letter of the alphabet based on how frequently they appear in the English language. We then take our chosen novel, go to a random page and start counting the letters in a line and that determines what is happening on the page. So this is a game that everyone can follow and play along with.

The best way to explain it is in an example.

First we set up what each of the letters mean:

- *A* = 1 run
- *B* = bowled
- *C* = caught
- *Everything else* = dot.

Then we take the first line of this chapter:

"Maths, after a certain age, becomes more about the .."

- *M* = dot
- *A* = 1
- *T, H, S* = dot

- $A = 1$

So the first over: is .1...1. A slow start but the batsmen are just testing the wicket.

Then we continue:

- F, T, E, R, A, C = ...1W. The opening batsman was caught at second slip. Score is 3-1.
- E, R, T, A, I, N = ...1

... as you can see one of the batsmen is about to be bowled in the next over. "It was an inswinging yorker. Unplayable." And so the story then goes on, for another 97 overs, and hopefully a last ball victory.

Of course we have to make the numbers mean more interesting things, and also to a certain extent randomise the game so that it makes it a bit more realistic, and hopefully our commentary team will give it colour and flavour.

Full disclosure: when I first tested this over 100 overs the team batting first posted 321-8 with the other team's reply being 148 all out. I wasn't really satisfied with that as a test and reran the second innings again and it was a nail biting last over finish of 312 all out. That's better. This testing is all in the hope of getting a reasonable scoring system in place to make the main action as realistic and likely as possible. Really I don't want a score of 500, or all out inside 10 overs.

In order to make it fairer and also more unpredictable I have introduced some randomisers. As every cricket fan knows this is a batsman's game; only they have options, but the bowlers can influence the game by taking wickets.

I have 2 types of batsman: Top Order and Tailender. Obviously, the former is more skilled than the latter and so gets 'out' less often and scores more runs. Furthermore the coach of the team can at any time switch the player from defensive to aggressive, which increases the scoring rate and the chance of getting out. They can be "switched" from their first ball, and once they have been switched they cannot be switched back. Batsmen at either end can be operating different styles, effectively like in a powerplay or towards the end of an innings. This will be decided by the coach during the game based on how they are doing. So we have 4 scoring systems that could be in play for each person:

	Top Order Batsman Defensive	Top Order Batsman Offensive	Tailender Defensive	Tailender Offensive
a	dot	dot	dot	dot
b	bowled	bowled	bowled	bowled
c	caught	caught	caught	caught
d	2	2	2	2
e	dot	dot	dot	dot
f	6	6	4	6
g	4	4	2	bowled
h	2	4	2	4
i	dot	dot	dot	dot
j	2	hole out	2	hole out
k	wicket	wicket	wicket	wicket
l	1	2	1	1
m	2	4	1	4
n	1	2	1	2
o	dot	dot	dot	dot
p	2	6	1	4
q	2	hole out	2	hole out
r	1	4	1	2
s	dot	dot	dot	dot
t	1	2	1	2
u	dot	dot	dot	dot
v	1 bye	2 bye	1 bye	2 bye
w	wide	wide	wide	wide
x	lbw	lbw	lbw	lbw
y	2	4	2	bowled
z	No ball	Run out going for 2	No ball	Run out going for 2

Each team can only pick six Top Order batsmen, and there has to be a normal balance to the team. There can be a maximum of 2 allrounders, who can be top-order batsmen and bowl, otherwise the top order can't bowl. So you need a minimum of 3 tailenders/bowlers, to get to the 50 overs.

Regarding the comments, each team has 1 review for LBWs, and the outcome will depend on the next letter. Z can be a free hit no-ball, in which case the player gets upgraded for the following ball but can't be out. Honestly I doubt we will get any x or z.

In order to add to the unpredictability, and to have some in-game action, for the first innings we will start on page 1. For the second innings we will start on page 2. We will then change the page and position with each wicket. We will choose a page based on the over of the innings that the batsman faces his first ball multiplied by their original position in the batting order. So if a batsman is promoted up to number 7, though were originally on the order at 9, and we are in the 35th over we will go to page 315 (9x35). We will start the tracking on the line of the over number that the bowler took the last wicket in. So, assuming the bowler is in his 8th over, we go to page 315 and line 8. This will allow the timing of a wicket to have a material effect on the game, as it does in reality, and strategically changing the batting order will also throw us to a different page. Remember different page = different story = different action.

The idea here is to create a game that can be followed by the reader if they have the original book, but also to highlight the fine line between success and failure, both in the sport and in its entertainment. In order to add to this, the gameplay therefore also must have a random element, a "the butterfly effect" to show the luck in sport. In the 2019 World Cup Final if the ball hadn't ricocheted off Ben Stokes' bat during the final over at the right speed and angle AND then travelled to the boundary, the game would have been over with New Zealand winning. The odds on a ball being thrown from that far away hitting a bat at that angle, and going to the boundary, as the game was on the line, are incalculably long and probably will never happen again. In theory the smallest butterfly, bird .. or pigeon flapping its wings on one side of the ground could have changed that ball's flight and thus the game. Therefore we will also have pigeons in this game, as protagonists in the action, a link for you to connect to in the real world @PigeonCricket, and most importantly to change the action and the events. At ball 200 in the first innings and ball 150 in the second innings there will be a "pigeon effect", a randomisation in the book cricket letters. To do this, on these balls, we will jump in the letters to the same place on the next page, starting a new string of letters, different action and a different script. Random, lucky and potentially leading to an unexpected and different result.

For this first adventure I will be using a copy of my wife's favourite book (and a global phenomenon), Harry Potter and the Deathly Hallows, written by JK Rowling. This book is certain to be a future English classic if it isn't one already. I suspect that Harry Potter uses more awkward letters than a traditional classic, and so we should get lots of action. "You're a wizard, Harry" would be 2..1..+.NB2122.112 = 15 runs in 18 balls, That's a T20 run rate.

Good luck to us all.

CHAPTER 1
PRE-MATCH

… "And that concludes the morning news for Wednesday June 19th 2030. Now over to Karen with the weather, what's it looking like?"

"Dez, as usual for London in June these days its warming up slowly though there's some cloud around. It doesn't look like there will be any rain and the sun should pop up from time to time. Current temperature around Covent Garden is a warm 13 degrees, though we expect a high of around 21 degrees by 2 o'clock this afternoon. Later on, in the week the weather is still looking good, though there is a chance of some rain coming into this weekend. It may be a bit cooler too. Don't worry we will keep an eye on it for you Dez, I know you are at the Oval on Sunday afternoon, back to you."

"Thanks Karen, if it only rains in the morning, we will be fine. Thanks to all our guests on the show this morning, you've been listening the breakfast show on 101.3 FM, Sports Radio, its five minutes past nine by my clock and now we hand you over to Pat and our team at Lord's for the start of the cricketing summer."

9:05   "Dez, Karen, good morning all, I'm Patty Pringle and welcome to Lord's, for the first ODI between England and India. What a summer we have in store for you. With both India and Pakistan touring the UK, this certainly will be a one to remember, and hopefully one for the record books. The Board of Control for Cricket in England, the BCCE, have really packed it in this summer, and with a total of 8 ODIs, 5 IT20s and 5 test matches it is going to stretch all of us deep into September. We start here today with the first of the one-day series between India and England as they compete for the biennial Jungan trophy brought to you this year with the support of the Levante Corporation. This is a three-match series, to be played over the coming week with the second ODI from Edgbaston on Friday afternoon, and the final game in the series from the Oval in South London on Sunday. Alongside me here as always, and keeping me company throughout the summer, is Jon Knight, England captain from 2016 to 2019 and winner of 2 Jungan trophies in the past. Good morning, Jon, looking forward to the summer?"

"Morning, Pat; you are right it is certainly going to be a brilliant summer, and if we can get the high-octane action of the previous few summers then I'm sure it will be great. India and Pakistan haven't both toured this country at the same time in 10 years and the spectacle of a showdown between them at Trent Bridge in September is going to be absolutely wild. But as you say we have a lot to get through before then. But yes: I'm ready. Cannot wait."

"The Jungan Trophy has produced some incredible memories in the past and we are looking to this one to be right up there. Before we delve into the teams and the details, and we have plenty of time to get through those, let's head straight out to Mike and Andy, who are out in the middle with the morning pitch report."

9:10 "Mornin' gents, yes I'm down here with the England hero of Sydney, former England captain, Andy Bird, and what a glorious day it is at the moment. A few clouds about but the sun is out and shining, making Lord's look absolutely majestic. The crowds are starting to make their way to their seats and I would say that we are about a quarter full at the moment. The Indian contingent are the only ones in here this early and the noise level is starting to pick up. Very different from when I was out here on my own 2 hours ago anyway. I expect they will be in full voice today. Andy, mornin' and welcome to the other side of the rope."

"Thanks Mike, and morning all, yes it's good to be behind the camera so to speak and I hope I can help make proceedings entertaining and exciting. Certainly the Indians do like to make some noise. They always bring noise with them. Given the number of them who show up here, and live locally, it always seems like these London games are their home games now. It's all part of the fun and what makes cricket so special."

"'Special' is the right word and Lord's is looking particularly good today. We are standing at the top of the wicket on the pavilion side, looking back towards the Levante Media Centre and the sun is just starting to peek through the clouds over the left of the pavilion behind us. So we will get a superb first look at this wicket. How's it looking Andy? This time last year you were out here analysing the pitch for the Kiwi ODI? If I remember, that day you won the toss and put them in?"

"Ha-ha: yes, and we got lucky that day. We were able to get over the line with some late heroics from Barney. Last year we were more in the middle of the square though, today we are using the third wicket from the left, though it still seems to be in good order. We would expect nothing less from the groundskeepers here, especially given the tech they have. This wicket looks a little green, and healthy in patches, which should see the ball bouncing around. As you know, Lord's has never spun very much for ODIs and really we need 3 days of test match play before it starts breaking up and ripping."

"So you think this is a seamers' paradise, get the ball swinging and seaming and batsman beware?"

"Hmm, I wouldn't say a paradise. It looks quite flat. I guess Angus will have asked Lord's for the biggest roller they have out here. The green will make the ball come onto the bat nicely, though as it softens up through the day there maybe some unevenness that comes through. I would have thought you would want to bat on it in the morning, and try and take advantage of some wicket help in the afternoon."

9:15   "For sure. We all know Angus will try and squeeze every advantage out of the set up as he can. Lord's though is all about this slope, no? How is that going to come into play?"

"There is so much advantage for bowlers from the pavilion end if they move the ball left to right down the slope into the right-hander.

But at this level they can all do that, and you are lucky if you have the bowling seniority and can demand that side. The real challenge is in the control from the other end, and if you can get any speed up the hill. But still I think I would choose to bat on this, the slope will still be there in the afternoon."

"Ok, thanks Andy. Pat, we have now made our way up to the other end of the wicket and looking down back towards the pavilion I can note that the boundary is really long on the leg side. From where we are, we have the pavilion in front of us, the Grandstand at the 'top of the slope' on the right, on the left the Mound and Tavern stands, and behind us the Edrich, Media Centre and Compton stands from left to right. As the wicket is 3rd in from the edge, the boundary down the slope looks like it is almost twice the length of the boundary in front of the Grandstand. Andy, from here the Grandstand is only looking like it's 50m away, that will surely be a target area, but up the slope means we may get some hole-outs out there too?"

"Yeah I'm sure that side of the ground will get some action. To be honest the way they have redesigned some of the stands here you get a good view from anywhere. It has almost become like a colosseum with the new towering Edrich and Compton stands. The downside is that we get a lot less of the elements down here. Less wind is great for batting but a bit unfair on the bowlers. Probably one of the reasons why we have seen so many records fall in the last few years. Mark Jules was great at using that to his advantage when he was forced to fight the slope in his early career."

"Jules will get the slope advantage now I presume, given how long he has been around! That's all from us right now, back to you guys in the studio."

Google Search: Angus Crickt ECB

Did you mean Angus Cricket BCCE? Showing results for Angus Cricket BCCE

Angus T. Merchant is an English current international cricket Head

Coach and formerly an international professional cricket player. He is currently the Head coach of the England, employed by the Board of Control for Cricket in England, a position he has had since 2024. For more information click here: http://pigeoncricket.com/team/eng/angusmerchant.

NEWS

NewsOnline: Angus Merchant says England are well prepared for their first ODI with India

AussieHerald: Merchant bullish about chances against India, expects a series win

IndiaNow: Merchant expecting to win? Hollier not taking the bait: fight will be won on the field

9:06   **Vikas @V4India:** @PPringles @SirJon I'm in! Only 6 mins in the queue today, straight in the Grace Gate. India Zindabad! Anyone else @HomeOfCricket this morning?

9:08   **toby @Tobytools:** @PPringles @SirJon Why does the BCCE always do this? They pack the summer and don't leave any space. What happens if it rains? Do they not live in the UK? What a complete bunch of clowns. Anyway, England have got this today.

9:09   **Vikas @V4India:** OMG! I just saw @jungan_cricket walking into the pavilion. What a legend. India owes you so much! Next time stop for a photo?

9:11   **toby @Tobytools:** @PPringles @SirJon Need you guys to be on form today! Boss didn't give me the day off. Stuck in the shop with the radio on. What happened to cricket on Freeview?

9:12   **Jon Knight @SirJon:** replying to @Tobytools Cricket must follow the $$$ to stay alive. If you want to watch it, pay up.

9:12   **toby @Tobytools:** replying to @SirJon I'm sure you aren't short of a few bob. Are you on the @LevantePvtInd gravy train too?

9:15   **kiks @nikita_aol:** @Mikedrop @abirdman @SirJon How can Angus influence @BCCElive? Shouldn't the pitch be neutral?

9:17   **Jon Knight @SirJon:** replying to @nikita_aol I'm pretty sure Angus has a lot of influence at the BCCE given that he was appointed Coach to make @BCCElive look good. Anyway the toss will be more important than the pitch.

9:18   **Vikas @V4India:** Great seats. Lower Grandstand. I can almost touch you from here @abirdman. Anyone else in this area?? Where are the Barmy Army setting up shop today? We need to fight them hard!

9:20   **toby @Tobytools:** @Mikedrop What does @abirdman know about reading a pitch? He chose wrong last year, got out cheaply and Barney had to come in and save the day as always. Let's hope Barney is in the same form today those record boards are calling. Do the opposite of whatever Andy says!

9:21   **kiks @nikita_aol:** @abirdman @Mikedrop India are in town to smash those Lord's honours boards. @jungan_cricket already on there, @CaptainSharma or @kumarRangersIPL will be up there by the end of the day.

9:20   "Thanks guys, really interesting stuff, plenty to think over for the captains and welcome to the team Andy. Jon, let me just pick up on something that the boys were talking about out there: is that short boundary going to be critical?"

"This is still a batsman-dominated game and if you give them easy opportunities then eventually they will start taking them. That boundary is short but from what the boys said, it seems that this is a pitch for batting all day on, so there should be lots of areas to score in. The lefties in particular should find that boundary pretty inviting. From up here we can see that the straight boundaries haven't been brought in that much, they are only off the edge by 2 or 3 metres. They are probably playing around 80m and are going to be tough to reach unless the ball is right in the slot."

"We will get all the information about the final team at the coin toss in about 10 minutes or so, though I think the English team has been quite settled for a while. I guess the only real change has come because of Andy's retirement over the winter. David Wigglesworth or Sam King are the probable replacements? They have both been in and around the squad for a couple of years now and have been scoring runs so are coming into form?"

"I would think it is between those two. The squad is settled and has experience and so they wouldn't want to make any wholesale changes. These two are very much in the future of this one-day set up but they are very different type of players. Both have scored runs but in different ways. Wigglesworth is the stronger and would probably be the preferred option given where the vacancy in the batting order is. He is more likely to pinch hit and get quick runs with the tail. King has a more traditional game. He is the one you want if you are chasing the game and you have limited wickets in hand. Very steady head for his age and would work to get you over the line."

"From a 'horses for courses' point of view I think I would probably go with King given his experience here with Middlesex? But I agree with you on Wigglesworth strength. If you have 5 overs left, he will get you more runs, if he doesn't give away his wicket. Perhaps Ray can jump in here? Yes, our stats guru Ray Dora is back with us this summer after taking the winter off. Some people it seems can give up 12 weeks touring down under for the misery of Yorkshire."

"Hi Pat, thanks for that and yeah it's good to be back. I'll happily take my Yorkshire farmhouse over trailblazing around Australia and New Zealand for 12 weeks lurching from hotel room to hotel room. I'm sure you were well taken-care of however by my Aussie colleagues. Getting back on point, Andy Bird will leave a big whole in that middle order. He gave it up at the top of his game, and over the last 12 months was averaging around 38 in ODIs. That is a bit lower than his career of 42, though not bad given that he was facing the Australians at home for most of it. That's going to be a big hole to fill. In last year's Hundred Wigglesworth really came to the fore and his hitting was able to get Manchester into the playoffs. He averaged in 45 in the round robin stage and had 2 scores above 70. In both of those he was able to carry his bat from the top of the order and get

Manchester into winning positions. He doesn't do as well chasing though. When there is a score on the board, he can't manage the situation and can come undone. A great example is that semi-final, they were only chasing 120, and he holed out going for cow corner for just 10. He will need experience to see how to manage situations, but this could be that opportunity. With so much batting ahead of him he won't have a lot of pressure on his shoulders, and the match could come down to him. King, on the other hand, barely featured in the Hundred last year. He is not that type of player. He has had an excellent run in the last few years in the Championship, the highlight being Middlesex's promotion to division 1 last year. He racks up the runs in a dignified and steady manner and I think he is the only player banging on the door of Andy's test spot. The reason why he is in the conversation for the ODI I suppose is because of his form. We have already had most of the domestic one-day season and he has been scoring runs freely, albeit against tier 2 bowlers. He has averaged closed to 55 in the 20 or so games he has played this year, and his average doesn't seem to move very much if he is setting or chasing. His average over the last few years has not been as good, around 35, but it may be worth sowing the seeds while he is in this purple patch. He has a calm head for the chase and will work well with the tail to get them over the line. Both have their strengths and in the end it will be up to Angus and William to make the call. Neither will be a bad choice."

9:25   "Thanks Ray, the question will be answered in just a few mins. The team sheets have been submitted and we will get our hands on them as soon as we can. In the meantime, we are counting down to the toss here at Lord's. Jon what would you do if you won it?"

"I think I would have to go with Andy and bat first. The pitch looks quite flat and I am not sure how much those grassy patches will support the bowler. Also looking upwards there doesn't seem to be much cloud cover so it shouldn't move around too much. Not that the white ball really does much anyway. I think the team batting first would normally have an advantage… That old adage of runs on the board."

"Ok we have the team sheets! England first: pretty much as expected, only the one change from the winter down under and it's King! He fills Andy's slot in the middle order and will shortly get his first ODI cap. Congratulations to him. So the full team sheet in batting order will be Tom Rhodes and Alex Quince to open, Hanson at 3, Barnes, Barney, at 4, they seem to have swapped around since Christmas, then Jones, Sherman, Sam King at 7, Mark Jules, Sonia Chancellor promoted one slot to 9, French at 10 and last but not least Mo Khan. Before I get your thoughts on the team, its toss time. The umpires and captains are about to come out into the middle and so we go back downstairs once again, to Mike."

Name	Bowling	Twitter	Age
Tom Rhodes			25
Alex Quince	Wicketkeeper		31
Greg Hanson		@hansomegreg	27
Ricky Barnes			28
William Jones	Captain	@billythekid	30
Patrick Sherman	Right Arm Medium		30
Sam King		@KingSamV	23
Mark Jules	Right Arm Fast	@jules_england	32
Sonia Chancellor	Right Arm Leg Spin	@glassceiling100	28
Hunter French	Right Arm Med-Fast	@frenchcricket	28
Mohammed Khan	Left Arm Fast	@MoKduck	25

9:21 **kiks @nikita_aol:** @PPringles @SirJon Short boundary for the lefties from the pavilion end but it's the same for everyone else coming from the other end!

9:21 **toby @Tobytools:** *replying to @nikita_aol* @SirJon has no idea. He just says the first thing that comes to his mind. Hope @abirdman is better.

9:23 **toby @Tobytools**: @PPringles Patty always goes with the safe option. Have some guts and pick @DavyW2018. He will take this Indian attack to pieces. The best horse is the one who can clear the ropes!

9:25 **Vikas @V4India:** Just connected to @PPringles commentary and I get 5 mins of nonsense from @dizzydora? Just give us numbers, man, and get off the stage. Who cares who they pick, probably won't bat and will field at 3rd man all day!

9:26 **toby @Tobytools:** *replying to @V4India* 100%. @dizzydora just loves the sound of his own voice. Shame no-one else does. @KingSamV is a Test player. Probably future @BCCElive captain. Wasted at number 7 in a one-day team.

9:26 **kiks @nikita_aol:** *replying to @Tobytools* Dave Wigglesworth is a classic choker!? Pick him, he will probably hole out today. Can't handle the pressure.

9:27 **toby @Tobytools:** @PPringles haha Frenchy got demoted behind @glassceling100. If you wanted a pat on the back from @BCCElive then that ain't gonna to do it.

9:28 **kiks @nikita_aol:** *replying to @Tobytools* @glassceiling100 was fantastic in the IPL. @CaptainSharma took her under his wing @Mumbai_IPL, and she was smashing it to all parts! Could teach @frenchcricket a few things.

9:30 **Vikas @V4India:** What about India? What's their order? @PPringles is so biased.

9:30 **toby @Tobytools** *replying to @nikita_aol* Yeah that was a steal from @Mumbai_IPL. Probably sold a million Sonia shirts, and barely had to pay for her in the auction. Ok she hit it around a bit, but the wickets were slow. If she gets in, she won't last long against the bouncers!

9:31 **Bobby @PigeonCricket** @Mikedrop @PPringles. Oi! I'm eating here umps! Wait.. I'm on TV!!! Hello World!! Hi Mum!

9:30 "Thanks Patty, and once again welcome down to the middle, everyone. We have the Toss party walking through the Long Room and down the pavilion steps. There is still lots of activity around the ground. The Indians are doing some fielding practice on the South side of the ground, in front of some noisy fans in the Tavern stand. Hollier and his team are knocking some long high catches to them, and fielding them back over a single stump. Wow that was a great throw back from Traheer, almost took out the stump. Over here on the right, in front of the Grandstand, we have the England team playing some five-a-side. Wrong sport, boys! It looks a bit intense Patty, let's hope none of them twist an ankle. The umpires are out onto the lawn and striding up towards me. Get out of the way pigeons. Randall nearly stepped on one there. So, the toss party as they are coming out, and it's a big party, Pat, Umpires' Randall and du Toit, alongside them His Royal Highness the Duke of Exeter, followed by our captains, Billy Jones and Sunil Sharma, with debutant Sam King. Trailing behind them, and in deep conversation about something, Rajiv Levante, chairman of the Indian Levante Group, and Bobby Jungan! That massive noise you just heard in the background was the Indian crowd in the Lower Grandstand getting their first view of Jungan as he came out. And nice guy that he is, he gave them a little wave, which has started to rile them up even more. Ex Indian Captain and legend, Bobby Jungan will be running the toss proceedings."

"Good Morning Ladies and Gentlemen, welcome to the toss of the first One Day International of this tri-match series between England and India, supported by Levante. What a lovely morning it is here at the home of cricket, and we are looking forward to a closely fought battle between these two teams. I'm sure you are all as excited as me. Let me first introduce the officiating panel, Umpire Faf du Toit, from South Africa, Umpire Theodore Randall from the West Indies, Captain of India Sunil Sharma, Captain of England William Jones, Chairman of the Board of Control for Cricket in England His Royal Highness the Duke of Exeter, and finally Mr Rajiv Levante, Chairman of the Levante Group. His Royal Highness will have the honour of the toss, and as the visiting captain, Sunil will have the call. Over to you, gents. The coin is up, and the call is heads. And it's tails. India have loss the toss. What will it be William?"

"We will bat."

"Thank you, and thank you very much to our toss party. England have won the toss and elected to bat first. Before we end the proceedings can I please ask William and His Royal Highness to present Sam with his first cap. Congratulations Sam and best of luck today. Sunil, William, Sam if you could wait behind a couple of minutes with Michael, and good luck to you all."

9:35   "Thanks Bobby, we will go to Captain Jones first who has chosen to bat first here. Tell us, why are you batting and what are you expecting today?"

"Thanks Mike, I think it was a relatively simple choice to bat first this morning. The pitch is looking quite flat and we don't think the wicket will throw up many surprises. It should be a good surface to bat on and the boys now have to go out there and do their work. The conditions are in our favour. It doesn't look like it will swing around too much and so we should be able to set a good score on here."

"What is a good score?"

"I think we will be targeting something 280 plus. Anything over 300 is very defendable on here and we will back ourselves to do the job if we can put up a score like that. But I think I would take 280 on the board if you offered it to me, so that will be our minimum target."

"Tell me why you chose Sam over David to fill Andy Bird's spot in the middle order? He provides some resistance rather than hard hitting?"

"Sam has been around the squad for a couple of years now, and I'm glad that we were able to give him the chance to play today. He has been scoring runs all over the domestic one-day comp and so comes into today with form. Being a Middlesex lad, Lord's is also home for him so that helps and hopefully that brings him some luck. Dave is also right up there and will definitely get his chance soon."

"We note that you have promoted Sonia Chancellor up the order a place, any reason why, is there an injury?"

"No, no, Frenchy is fine. He wouldn't be in the 11 if he had a niggle as we will need the full 10 overs from him. Since the winter, Sonia has really upped her batting, as we saw in the IPL. She was smashing it around and is full of confidence. We want her to bring that confidence into today, but obviously hope that she won't need to put on the pads today if the top order can get the job done."

9:40 "You have also swapped Hanson and Barnes around?"

"It's all about where the boys feel comfortable. They sat down with Angus in March and had a chat about which way around they wanted to go. Barney batted up at 3 for most of last year and was doing well, but Greg hasn't been so comfortable at 4. He is an opener at heart and so likes the ball to be a bit harder and come onto the bat. Still I have faith in both of them, and they will deliver where they bat."

"This is your first official series stepping up into the captain's shoes how are you feeling?"

"They are big shoes to fill. It's definitely a change and to be honest I didn't really know how much background work Angus and Andy used to do. The preparation workload is tough though I'm loving it. It's also great to have the full support of Quincy as vice and behind the stumps, he sees a lot from there and really helps me out."

"Thanks Bill, I'll let you go and re-join the boys upstairs and get them ready. Captain Sharma, come over next. Wow listen to that noise from the crowd! Are you and the boys up for it today?"

"Yes, very much so. I have full faith in the team, and we have been through the correct build-up and planning. The team has been in England since the end of the IPL and have gotten a feel for the conditions and the bouncing ball. The warmup games have been useful in settling down our batting order and we should be ok. I mean better than ok!"

"You certainly have the crowd support, is this a home game?"

"We always travel very well when we come to the UK. There are so many Indian cricket fans in London and around the country. We appreciate all their support of course and hopefully can encourage us across the time. Although I wouldn't say Lord's is as much home for us as Edgbaston is!"

"Are you scared of facing Jules and Khan out here? England kept them away from the warm-up matches so you wouldn't get a feel for them?"

"Ha-ha, no, not scared of them. We know Mo very well from his time playing in IPL and obviously Jules has been around for ages, and we have come up against him a few times over the years. For sure they are both very different in these conditions, but I don't think they will worry the boys too much. Of course we will give them the respect they deserve, but not much more than that. If they miss their lines we will be ready. They know the ball flies off our bats just as quickly as it comes onto it."

"It feels like Kumar is on form at the moment?"

"Very much so: he has had a great few months. He captained the Goa Rangers to their title and really led from the front at the top of the order. He batted well in the warmup game here so is getting his eye well trained to these different wickets. As you saw, he has also been giving the crowds lots of catching practice, which is his style of play very aggressive and positive. Jules should be scared of him."

"And just before we let you go get ready, how was playing with Sonia in Mumbai?"

"Well she is a true professional to be honest, and we had a great time. It was her first IPL and everyone was unsure of what to expect, but as a team we took a chance on her, and it worked really well. The fans absolutely loved her and I think she was more of an attraction than me when we were touring. There were crowds lining the streets whenever we rolled into town. Certainly, she has changed the game for all of us and she is setting a great example for a lot of young girls out there"

"Can you pick her googly?"

"I am getting better at it! We got to spend a lot of time in the nets with her, so we should know everything about her. I'm sure she will have some tricks up her sleeve though. Doesn't turn as much here as it does back home so she will have to be careful."

"Thanks Sunil, I'll let you get back to the team and start preparing, and we will see you back down here with the team in 20 minutes or so. Sam King, you're next; welcome to the big leagues, ready to go?"

"Yeah, can't wait Mike. Really want to thank Billy and Angus for giving me the chance. Hopefully I can do them and the team proud if my turn comes."

"You have been scoring lots of runs here while the boys have been away in India, do you think that will help?"

"Hopefully yes, the domestic attacks are still very strong even if most of the boys have been called up to the IPL, so I hope that experience and knowledge helps me out. Middlesex have done well here in the last few years so I can take some confidence in being a part of that. Angus has also really been supportive of the boys around the squad, giving us advice, support, whatever we need, so we are ready to step in when called upon."

"Will you be able to step up to an international level attack like the ones India have brought?"

"Don't have much choice. I've been facing Khan and Pooran on the simulator, so I know what to expect but it's different in reality. If I go through my normal routine and clear my mind I'll be ok. To be good at this game you need to challenge yourself and step up. I'm ready for that next challenge and I hope I can help the team over the line."

"Thanks Sam, get back up there and get ready. Good luck for today. Pat, that's all from down here in the middle, back up to you."

9:32   **Vikas @V4India:** @PPringles Crowd around me went crazy when @Jungan_Offical came out of pavilion. No one is watching England 5-a-side. Hopefully Hanson tackles Sherman and puts him out of the game.

9:32   **kiks @nikita_aol:** @Mikedrop Its TrahAr not TrahEEr.

9:33   **kiks @nikita_aol:** @PPringles @Mikedrop The old Duke man is looking a bit weak. Is he limping around? Poor guy, tough couple of years!

9:34   **kiks @nikita_aol:** @CaptainSharma is looking fiiiiiine today. If @pinkyoffical ever gets too boring I'm available!

9:34   **Vikas @V4India:** @PPringles @SirJon India batting first! England can't chase, this game is already over.

9:37   **toby @Tobytools:** @CaptainSharma was barely tested in the warmup games. They got cheap runs against average attacks. @billythekid kept his aces in his hand. A couple of head-height bouncers from @MoKduck and then he will be scared.

9:38   **toby   @Tobytools:**   @PPringles   @Mikedrop @kumarRangersIPL is so overrated. Just because he can bash it around in the IPL on slow wickets, doesn't count for anything when the ball is swinging around corners.

9:38   **Vikas @V4India:** @Mikedrop @glassceiling100's googly is sooo obvious. You can see it coming from the stands. Open your eyes @CaptainSharma

9:40   **toby @Tobytools:** *replying to @V4India* I would take one of her googlies any day, if you know what I mean. She can promote my order!

9:41   **toby @Tobytools:** @Mikedrop @SirJon they should promote Greg to the top of the order. Chuck Quince down to 6, and then we won't have to watch that stupid dance he does.

9:42   **Vikas @V4India:** *replying to @Tobytools* Are you a child? What does that even mean?

9:43   **kiks @nikita_aol:** @Mikedrop @KingSamV doesn't have a clue what he is in for. @azerXpress is unplayable for pace. Pooran will bounce him right out. Simulators don't bounce very much do they!?

9:44   **Jon Knight @SirJon:** *replying to @Tobytools* Stupid Dance? It's called a trigger movement! Gets him lined up correctly and moving forward, its textbook. He's done great at the top of the order.

Google Search: is Sonia Chancellor ..

Is Sonia Chancellor on drugs
is Sonia Chancellor a lesbian
<u>is Sonia Chancellor married</u>
is Sonia Chancellor Indian
Sonia Chancellor, née Patel, is married to Liam Chancellor, an outsourcing consultant based in London. They were married in January 2028 and have 1 son. For more information click here *http:// pigeoncricket.com/team/eng/soniachancellor*

NEWS

NewsOnline: Sonia Chancellor to start for England against India

TimesSport: Chancellor opens up about cricket tours and being away from family

IndiaNow: Sonia Chancellor wins upcoming player of the year in the IPL

9:45 "Welcome back everyone, and before we get into analysing the teams, let me give you the Indian team sheet in batting order. At the top of the order we have Kumar and Kapoor, Ankit Bihari third, followed by Captain Sharma. Trahar at 5, AP Singh at 6, who will also take the gloves, Nikil Panda at 7, Shubanka at 8 with Mopal, Pooran and Khan bringing up the tail. I am also pleased that Bobby Jungan has rushed upstairs from his official engagements in the middle to join us in the commentary box. Bobby Jungan is an ex captain of India, and son of the late Parvinder Jungan, who this trophy is named after. Bobby: great to have you with us this summer, and first over to you, what do you think of the Indian line up?"

Name	Bowling	Twitter	Age
Ravi Kumar		@kumarRangersIPL	30
Rohan Kapoor			26

			28
Ankit Bihari			28
Sunil Sharma	Captain	@CaptainSharma	32
SK Trahar		@SK_KolkotaKing	25
A P Singh	Wicketkeeper	@anothersingh20	30
Nikil Panda	Right Arm Offspin	@GreatWhitePanda	29
Shubanka	Right Arm Legspin		24
Varun Mopal	Right Arm Med-Fast		31
Deepak Pooran	Right Arm Fast		27
Azer Khan	Right Arm Fast	@AzerXpress	30

"Thanks Patty, its great to be here. The Indian line up is pretty much as expected and basically the same eleven that they played in Canterbury, during the warmup. Bihari is back in now that his side strain has healed and Umesh will be doing the drinks duties. India will miss what Umesh can do with the ball and his experience in English conditions, but you can't leave out Bihari if he is fit."

"Pat, let me jump in here. Bobby, this is not a strong bowling attack. I expected India to make more changes given the conditions they are playing in? These guys are fast but they lack control and can't really put much movement on it?"

"I think they have to go with their best attack and this is it. Maybe on a bouncy Oval wicket or small Trent Bridge ground you choose others, but here I think you put out your best and ask them to step up. My only concern really is Mopal. He had a lot of overs in the IPL and given the party in Goa after they won, only made it out here a couple of weeks ago. He hasn't had as much acclimatisation as the rest of the group. Umesh, who had a fantastic IPL, could have filled his spot and added something with the bat, but Sharma clearly thinks Mopal is the better pick."

"Two spinners in these conditions is crazy?"

"Ok; there I agree. It looks a bit strange at Lord's to have two, especially against such destructive batsmen. If the pitch doesn't spin then it is a very big risk as you don't have anyone else to turn too. I guess they have tried to read the pitch the best they can and see something the rest of us can't?"

"Great to see you guys going at it already! We like a bit of spice, on the pitch and up here! England are out first with the bat so let's talk about their top 6, what sort of score could they make out here, what do they need?"

"I think they need about 300 as a target, batting first on this flat surface. I think Jon would almost call this a road. Times have changed in one-dayers since we played and the 400 scores are less common now, unless all the boundaries are at 50 metres. The bowlers have become savvier and have a lot of variation to make it confusing. You don't get six sixes in an over anymore, hardly ever more than two. If the openers can put up 60-70 in the first powerplay with maybe the loss of only one wicket that gives them a real chance at 300+. They have so many caps and some much needed experience at 3, 4, and 5 and that's where the real damage will be done. Hanson, Barnes and Jones, if they turn up then this will be a big score. England don't bat deep though with Sherman a bit of a loose cannon and Sam King untested at this level, then we are into the bowlers."

9:50   "Yes I agree, that seems about the right mark. If they can get up to 320 or beyond then India will struggle to chase it down. Ray, you have some numbers for us?"

"Yes Pat, thanks – I have the data on the last 10 one-dayers here. We only play one a year these days so have to go quite far back, and it looks like the team batting first won in 7 out of 10 of them. This being said England chased down the Kiwis here last year, and the year before South Africa chased down England's weak 135. So, the last 2 have gone to the team batting second, but most of the rest of this decade has gone to the team setting the targets. Other than those 2, England chased down Pakistan's 289 in 2025. The average score in the first innings here over the last 10 games is around 259, which includes the 190 that the Kiwis posted last year and the 135 from the year before. The rest of the scores have been between 230 and 300 with the top score in 2021 when the Aussies posted that massive 368. I think that was a different era of cricket though, before the new equipment regulations came in. In 2027 the Australians got close to

England's 262, so I would say to be safe anything over 280 will be an uphill battle."

"Thanks Ray, keep them coming. The players have started coming out of the pavilion and have started lining up for the national anthems. I think we have a couple of minutes to talk about the Indian bowling attack before the festivities begin. Jon, can India restrict England to less than 280?"

"The conditions are not perfect for bowling. Sharma would have liked a bit more cloud cover, and perhaps for it to be a bit warmer for his Indian bowlers, though they have a chance. The white ball will move for the first 5-10 overs from each end and that's the window that Khan and Pooran will have to get it done. If they are only 1 or 2 down at 20 overs then it will be tough. Playing 2 spinners on this surface is a risk because it will not turn that much, but there is a part of me that thinks Panda is mainly in the team for his batting rather than his off breaks. The spinners maybe able to slow down the scoring in the middle few overs though I doubt this pitch will do anything in terms of wickets. If England go after the spinner though, watch out in the Grandstand. Bobby?"

"For sure they will give it a go. They have to, that's why they are here. And they are experienced enough in these conditions and on this type of surface. The odds are very much with the batsmen, that's what you get for winning the toss, though that can be flipped quickly with some early wickets."

9:55 "Thanks guys, yes its going to be a great contest. That brings us nicely to the end our pregame coverage of England versus India. Play is just around the corner after the national anthems, which will be sung by award-winning soprano Kathryn Coleman. Don't forget; throughout the day you can engage directly with us here in the studio by email, cricket@sportsradio.com; or on twitter @PPringles. We would love to hear from you and get your take on what's happening. In the meantime I will hand back to Dez at headquarters for the 10am news and I will be back in just a few minutes alongside Andy Bird for the first action of the day."

9:46   **Vikas @V4India:** Finally @PPringles gives Indian batting line up. A winning line up. Boom boom at the top, quality in the middle, and power at the end. They will chase anything England post.

9:47   **kiks @nikita_aol:** @Jungan_Official is a really good speaker on radio! Very clear and makes great analysis. Also he is happy to tell @SirJon where to shove it.

9:48   **toby @Tobytools:** *replying to @nikita_aol* Not that I ever want to agree with @SirJon, but he is right. India have chosen the wrong bowling attack for this pitch. Umesh would have been a better pick than Mopal. More aggressive and more likely to take wickets.

9:51   **kiks @nikita_aol:** @SirJon you are actually given credit to the Indian team? Wow. Didn't think I would see the day.

9:52   **Vikas @V4India:** Oh here we go again with @dizzydora and his numbers. Stop calling on him @PPringles. Just ask him for his excel sheet and done. England won't get to 200 and this game will be over by 3pm.

9:53   **toby @Tobytools:** Useless contributions from @SirJon. Obviously there is nothing in it for the bowlers. That's what everyone has been saying for the last hour. If @glassceiling100 takes any wickets today I'll quit my job.

9:55   **Vikas @V4India:** @PPringles @Jungan_Official England have no depth to their batting at all. Sherman, @KingSamV, @jules_england, @glassceiling100, none of them can bat.

9:56   **kiks @nikita_aol:** @PPringles why did you give out your twitter accounts? We are going to be flooded by clowns now. Like this @Tobytools character! Wouldn't know the right end of a cricket bat if it hit him in the face!

9:56   **Vikas @V4India:** @PPringles I hope that @abirdman give us some good gossip from inside the England camp. He must know all those guys well. There must be someone that everyone hates?

9:57   **Vikas @V4India:** @PPringles Chakde India! Jana Gana

Mana Adhinayaka Jaya He. We Salute you!

9:58 **Pri @pinkyofficial:** Oh god! Just got here and missed @katycoleman! Bloody driver just went around in circles. I want a private performance babe! Good Luck @CaptainSharma and Go India!! #katy #katycoleman #BFF #loveyoubabe #ENGIND #GoIndia #sunnyandpri #levante

9:58 **toby @Tobytools:** *replying to @V4India* Its probably not good etiquette to tweet during the national anthem if you care so much!

9:59 **Jon Knight @SirJon:** *replying to @nikita_aol* We need some more people so we can drown @Tobytools out. No respect for the game.

10:00 **toby @Tobytools** *replying to @SirJon* $£%@ you!!

10:00 **Twitter:** @Tobytools This tweet has been deleted for breaching our terms and conditions.

CHAPTER 2
ENGLAND 0/0, INDIA YET TO BAT

10:00   "Welcome back everyone I'm Patty Pringle and if you are just joining us we are at Lord's for the 1st One Day International of the Jungan Series between India and England. England won the toss and elected to bat. Tom Rhodes will face the first ball from Azer Khan, bowling from the pavilion end. Umpire du Toit signals play!"

Khan to **Rhodes**, 1 run, loose ball on the pad, clipped down to fine leg, fielded by **Pooran.**

"Khan is bowling to an aggressive 7-2 field. A reminder for our listeners we start the innings in the first of 2 powerplays. This is an automatic powerplay from overs 1-10 where there are only 2 fielders allowed outside the 30 yard circle."

Khan to **Quince**, 2 runs, loose ball on the pads, picked up early as drifting down, steps across and defends it down the hill through the vacant midwicket area. **Mopal** gives chase and catches up just before the ropes.

"Going around the ground, we have Singh behind the stumps. 2 slips, backward point, cover, extra cover, mid-off, mid-on, all inside the circle. Then a regulation 3rd man and wide fine leg. Sharma, the Indian captain is at mid-off, and already in discussions with the bowler as he walks back to his mark."

Khan to **Quince**, no run, wider outside of the off stump, left alone, through to the keeper.

Khan to **Quince**, 1 run, in swinging on middle stump, defended with soft hands just in front of square leg. Fielder **Pooran**, cleans up as they jog through for 1.

Khan to **Rhodes,** wide ball, inswinging down the legside and left alone as he stepped across his stumps. Good take by **Singh** as the ball was moving away from him. Du Toit spreads his wings to make the signal to the pavilion, and to the scorer's box just under the Old Father Time clock.

Khan to **Rhodes**, no run, outswinger outside off stump, back of a length and left alone.

Khan to **Rhodes**, 2 runs, lovely shot, outside the off stump, but too full. Shown the full face of the bat and guided nicely between cover and point. Up the hill to the short boundary, but slowing down and won't quite reach. Fielded by **Panda** from backward point, and thrown in by **Kapoor** who was also giving chase.

10:04   England 7-0 after 1 over. "Andy, welcome to the studio. Looks like Khan hasn't quite warmed up yet?"

"Hi Patty, yes that looked like a warm-up over. Which is not great at this level. Giving these batsmen any chance to get their eyes in is dangerous. He just doesn't seem to have control of the ball or the conditions yet. Perhaps its swinging around more than he expected. Sharma was straight up in his face after the first couple and he did straighten up after that. As expected Pooran is going to take the other new ball from the nursery end."

Pooran to **Quince**, no run, shortish, outside the off stump and left alone, with arms raised.

"Pooran has opted for a more conservative 6-3 field. He still has the 2 slips though has more protection on the short legside boundary. They have taken out cover and swapped him across to midwicket. It looks more balanced though there is a big inviting gap down the hill through the covers which may bring the slips into action."

Pooran to **Quince**, 1 run, defended into the covers and they scamper through for 1.

Pooran to **Rhodes**, no run, good length on middle, defended straight back to the bowler.

Pooran to **Rhodes**, 2 runs, outswinger outside off stump, good length, gently cut into the offside where it runs down the hill. **Trahar** chases after it and collects just before the boundary in front of the Mound Stand. They run the first hard and jog the second as the throw comes into the keeper end.

Pooran to **Rhodes**, 2 runs, outswinger again, short length, cut off the back foot towards the Mound Stand. **Trahar** chases again and throws it to the keeper. **Pooran** is furious with himself and stand with hands on hips in the middle of the wicket, forcing the batsmen to run around him.

Pooran to **Rhodes**, no run, full deliver on middle and off stump. Up at 89mph, calmly defended out into the offside.

10:09   England 12-0 after 2 overs. "Pooran is starting to get up to his speed now Andy?"

"We know he can get over 90. He is the fastest of the Indian bowlers and with that height can give it some bounce too. He was building up the speed in that over, but remember it's cold out there for the Indians. Most of them are in full jumpers. Having run to the boundary twice Trahar took off his full knit jumper to reveal a sleeveless one underneath! It will take a couple of overs though we should see some low 90s from Pooran by over 3 or 4. Khan on the other hand just needs to keep it straighter."

Khan to **Quince**, no run, on off stump moving away, left alone.

Khan to **Quince**, 1 run, on middle stump, defended into the open leg side, fielded by **Mopal**, coming around from wide mid-on.

Khan to **Rhodes**, no run, wide outside off stump, back of a length, through to the keeper at head height.

Khan to **Rhodes**, 2 runs, full and on the pads, worked onto the leg side through forward square leg. Its quick down the hill, but **Pooran** makes a good dive to stop the boundary. They manage to get a second run as the fielder gets up and gets the throw in.

Khan to **Rhodes**, no run, slower ball, full on middle stump, defended back to the bowler. Fielder **Mopal** charges in to pick it up for him.

Khan to **Rhodes**, no run, short ball on off stump, defended off the back foot out to **Panda** at point.

10:13   England 15-0 after 3 overs. "Pat, that's much better from Khan. Starting to find his length and his speed variations. Seems like he is getting it to move too. This may not be a done deal for the batsmen you know! That top of off stump is all he should be looking for, and he found it 5 out of 6 balls in that over."

Pooran to **Quince**, 1 run, good length and line, though squeezed out into the covers for an easy single.

Pooran to **Rhodes**, no run, 88mph yorker length on off stump, great delivery. Bat just gets down in time and the ball trickles out to **Panda** at point.

Pooran to **Rhodes**, 6 runs, smashed into the Grandstand. Slower ball at 73mph and just way too short with no protection on the boundary. Picked early and heaved off the back foot over the deep midwicket fence. "Go fetch that" he stares back at the bowler who has his head in his hands.

Pooran to **Rhodes**, 1 run, gets off strike quickly after the big hit, good length on middle and defends it into the cover area, for a quick single. **Trahar** the fielder.

Pooran to **Quince**, no run, straight and fast, back of a length, defended out to midwicket where **Kapoor** is quickly in.

Pooran to **Quince**, wide, tries to entice the batsman outside of the off stump, with a full delivery. Umpire Randall signals wide. The bowler doesn't want to believe it. Sharma talks to the **Umpire Randall** and he gestures that it was outside of the track line.

Pooran to **Quince**, 2 runs, straightened up but still a bit loose outside the off stump. There is some bat on ball and it runs past backward point who gives chase. **Mopal** runs around from 3ʳᵈ man to cut off the boundary and **Panda** gets the ball back in. **Pooran** stares at **Quince**, as he runs past him smirking. They both know it was a bit edgy and could have gone anywhere.

10:18   England 26-0 after 4 overs. "England will be very pleased with the start they are having, although India won't be too disheartened either. Apart from a couple of poor bowling decisions they have been tight and they could have had a wicket. Andy are you starting to get an idea for this wicket now and how it is playing?"

"It seems to be in good order as we suspected, though there is something there for the bowlers, I can feel it. They will need to get build some pressure on the batsmen before they can get their tails up though these new balls are doing something. Khan to continue from the pavilion end."

Khan to **Rhodes**, no run, great delivery, outswinger on the off stump on a good length, played and missed. Comes within inches of the edge of the bat before swinging away and taken between the keeper and 1ˢᵗ. The whole slip cordon have their hands on their heads and the bowler gives a wry smile towards the batsman, as he walks down and taps the pitch mark.

Khan to **Rhodes**, 1 run, short delivery on middle stump, defended in to the legside and they come through for a run as **Mopal** comes around to field.

"Sharma is making a change in the field for Quince now. He moves across to midwicket and pushes the offside fielders around a bit so they cover more ground. Pat I think he is starting to get scared of Quince's trigger movement. That step he has gets him on the front foot and more on the offside, but that also allows him to open up the legside for anything that is on middle or worse. I have seen him take balls from off stump out there too, so I am not surprised that Sharma is choosing to balance the field."

Khan to **Quince**, no run, off stump line, defended to **Kapoor** in the covers on the front foot.

Khan to **Quince**, no run, swinging in onto a middle stump line, defended out into the leg side where **Sharma** is quickly in.

Khan to **Quince**, 6 runs, no you can't bowl there! Great shot. Full on off stump, clears the front leg and full swing through the line. Ball is up high for a very long time and comes down onto the advertising hoardings. Trahar was effectively a wide mid-off and so had no chance, it was a high risk shot, but well executed.

Khan to **Quince**, no run, good reply from the bowler, short and fast, right into the chin area, as the batsman triggers across to middle. Gets the bat high and defends it down straight.

10:06   **kiks @nikita_aol:** @abirdman @PPringles Azer needs to find his line. This is useless stuff. Is @CaptainSharma going to plug that massive hole in the leg side?

10:08   **Vikas @V4India:** *replying to* @nikita_aol Azer needs to bowl better. He needs to bowl to the field he has set!

10:10   **toby @Tobytools:** @abirdman @PPringles these Indians look pretty chilly out there. Seems like ideal BBQ weather to me!

10:10   **kiks @nikita_aol:** @abirdman @SirJon great dive from Pooran. How did he manage to get down to that?? Needs to be careful he doesn't pull something

10:17   **Jon Knight @SirJon:** *replying to* @nikita_aol That's what you get for diving around on the floor.. next over you get dispatched into the stands!

10:18   **Vikas @V4India:** *replying to* @SirJon Just one bad ball! He will shake it off.

10:18   **Craig @barmy1992:** *replying to* @SirJon It's raining sixes in the sunshine!! @barmyGeoff almost took a blinder 10 rows back. Wouldn't trust him to catch a cold mind!

10:20   **kiks @nikita_aol:** @abirdman What a delivery from Azer! Swing and a miss. Rhodes had no idea where that was going.

10:21 **Vikas @V4India:** @PPringles @SirJon Mopal seems to be all over the field! I had no idea he could cover so much ground!

10:23 **Jon Knight @SirJon:** *replying to @V4India* Mopal has to cover the whole legside when Khan is bowling, and the third man boundary from the other side. ... and I guess he will have to do some bowling soon too!

10:23 **Geoff @barmyGeoff:** *replying to @barmy1992* I would have caught that one down mid-off's throat! Shame Quince couldn't get it into the stands again, but anything over the rope we will take! The boys are rolling now!

10:24 England 33-0 after 5 overs. "They are building a great foundation here Andy, and it doesn't seem like they are taking too many risks? A couple of close calls, but they have given the bad balls what they deserve. And they are running well between the wickets."

"Yes it's a great base to build from, but wickets can come like London buses. None for a while and then 2 or 3 in a row. Patty, I'm going to give my seat up to Bobby Jungan now, so I'll catch up with you in a while."

Pooran to **Rhodes**, wide, short pitching on middle. Goes for a big cross bat slog but gets nothing of it and it flies just past the ribcage down the leg side. **Umpire Randall** makes the signal that everyone is expecting.

Pooran to **Rhodes**, 2 runs, **chance** for a run out, straighter on off stump, dabbed down just forward of point and **Quince** calls from the non-striker's end through for a run, **Panda** is round in a flash, picks and throws at the keepers end, ball misses and runs down to fine leg giving the batsmen a chance to get an overthrow.

Pooran to **Rhodes**, no run, lots of aggression now as an angry **Pooran** throws down a 91mph bouncer. It's not that well directed though and is left alone outside off stump. **Singh** has to take the ball above his head.

Pooran to **Rhodes**, 1 run, good running, full pitched on off stump, soft hands with the defensive shot and sets off immediately as the ball travels out to mid-off on the circle. **Sharma** on his heels takes too long to get there and they are comfortably through.

Pooran to **Quince**, 2 runs, straight bat straight drive past the bowler just on the leg side. It's a long boundary towards the Levante Media Centre and both **Sharma** and **Shubanka** give chase. They work together to stop the ball before the rope and get it back to the bowler quickly, with **Shubanka** committing to the dive.

Pooran to **Quince**, no run, a fierce delivery clocking 91.2mph, just back of a length and this time well directed over off stump, easy to sway away though, the keeper takes it above his head.

Pooran to **Quince**, no run, a bit slower at 88mph this one, but back of a length and rising on middle. Can't be avoided and is played down from chest height into the legside. Good end to the over.

10:31 "England 39-0 after 6 overs. Bobby, welcome back into the booth. We have the replay from the shy at the stumps just coming through now. The throw was a bit wild as we know, but as it comes in we can't see Quince in the frame yet, rolling forward a bit there is the lunge from the batsman with the outstretched bat and I think he would have been just short? A chance there?"

"Patty, that's not the greatest camera angle. We can see the lunge but it's hard to tell if the ball has passed the stumps or not. Ah ok, this one should confirm it. Yep rocking and rolling it through those frames he would have been about 2 inches short. Close call and dangerous running, though I expected better from Panda. On his preferred arm he should have gotten closer. I'm not saying he would have hit the stumps, but he's one of the best fielders on that team so miss by that much is a bit embarrassing."

"It looks like Khan is going to change his angle to Rhodes here, and will come right arm around the wicket. Khan has put the leg side protection in for Quince though doesn't have it for Rhodes. Sharma himself is doing the running around between balls, fielding at midwicket for Quince and then mid-off for Rhodes."

Khan to **Rhodes**, 2 runs, a good ball but swung in too much and is clipped off the pads through midwicket and down the hill. Another big chase for **Mopal,** though the ball is slowing down as it leaves the square and heads into the outfield. The batsmen come back for a comfortable 2, with the throw into the bowler's end.

Khan to **Rhodes**, no run, better direction towards off stump and just back of a length, a bat is dangled out away from the body, though nothing connects and the ball goes through to the keeper. The bowler liked that one and has a spring in his step.

Khan to **Rhodes**, 1 run, **chance** through the vacant 3rd slip area, thick edge off a beautiful ball. Pitched on middle and off stump and seemed to surprise the batsman with some extra bounce. **Kumar** at second slip gave it a good dive with one hand though couldn't get near it, and he is picked up off the floor by his slips partner, **Bihari**. The bowler should feel very hard done by there, and the ball is collected at third man by **Shubanka**. Good battle brewing between **Khan** and **Rhodes**.

Khan to **Quince**, 1 run, back over the wicket and it's short and into the chest, above his average 83mph pace at 87. Fended off into the square leg area and called though for a quick single as **Sharma** cleans up.

Khan to **Rhodes**, no run, short and fired up at the rib cage from around the wicket. Defended down back into the bowler's follow through and picked up on the run, with a fake shy at the stumps. Smiles all around, though the bowler senses something here.

Khan to **Rhodes**, 1 run, pressure off on the last ball of the over, wasn't a good one. Wide of off stump and moving away towards 2nd slip, the ball is guided behind point down to third man with little risk. **Shubanka** runs around and gets the ball in over the stumps before they are able to come back for the second.

10:35   England 44-0 after 7 overs. "Patty, that was a great over from Khan, the change of angle has worked well. It stops Rhodes from setting up to open that leg side and has put him under much more pressure. That whole area across the square and down the hill towards the Tavern stand is so vacant and inviting, and from this angle anything attempted down there will bring the slips into play. I would be tempted for the next over to try a 3rd slip or a gully, perhaps sacrifice extra cover?"

"He is becoming really ferocious too, picking up the speed and getting his tail up. Andy Bird was just on here before you talking about that and the momentum shift that these bowlers need to capitalise on. It wasn't a cheap over, though the scorecard of 2, dot, 1, 1, dot, 1, doesn't tell the whole picture. Anyway, we are going to have our first change at the nursery end. As they like to do in the early overs, India are going to bring on the offspinner Panda. Lots of arm waving and movement going on as they get their field right, and the 12th man is bringing lots of helmets out. I think this is going to be an aggressive field."

Panda to **Rhodes**, 1 run, floated outside off stump and driven slowly to mid-off right on the circle and an easy single.

"Ok, so the field Panda is going with is a 5-4 with men everywhere. Not sure if there is a plan here. We have 1st slip, men around the bat at silly point and short leg, a cover, mid-off and mid-wicket on the edge of the circle, and the 2 deep men on the square leg boundary and at deep mid-on. Is that everyone? Wait, that makes 8, so there should be one more, ah, Khan at short fine leg, or a sort of fly leg slip. Not sure what he is doing there; on the edge of the circle would be better."

Panda to **Quince**, 2 runs, darted at middle stump, no spin and driven to the right of cover and into the gap. The outfield is very slow down towards the Mound Stand and the ball stops short of the ropes, fielded by **Sharma** from mid-off, though with enough time to come back for 2.

Panda to **Quince**, no run, much better ball, bit of flight and some turn, pitching outside off and turning to middle. A solid forward defensive, gives the ball the respect it deserves, and it is picked up by **Kumar** at short leg.

Panda to **Quince**, 1 run, over-pitched and picked early, mistimed though and only goes through into the extra cover gap in time for no more than a single. Fielded by **Kapoor** who hits the stumps with a shy at the bowlers end, starts his celebration before realising that the batsman is already way past the umpire.

Panda to **Rhodes**, no run, back on a good length and some nice turn and bounce, the ball is defended down to **Kumar** at short leg with no risk.

Panda to **Rhodes**, 1 run, too straight and with some turn the ball is guided off the pads down past **Khan** at short fine leg, he has to turn and recover quickly though Quince is through for the single.

10:38   England 49-0 after 8 overs. "Pooran's first spell was 3 overs, no maidens, none for 22, very expensive, and you can see why Sharma wanted a change. Good opening over from Panda, he is finding some turn?"

"It is always difficult for the off spinner from that nursery end as they have to sort of turn it up the hill. There were a few balls there where he was putting the revolutions on it, but they were just going on straight and were easy to play. This being said one of the spinners would need to take this end and I don't think Shubanka the leg spinner would be safe with that short Grandstand boundary. So Panda is taking one for the team here, but doing a nice enough job. It's an aggressive field Sunil has given him, so he is going to be expensive, just hopefully can break this partnership down. I'm glad Khan is continuing from the pavilion end, he is bouncing around at the top of his mark and isn't tired yet, the battle continues."

Khan to **Rhodes**, 1 run, too straight with that much open space on the leg side, played nicely off the pads into the vacant midwicket area and **Mopal** fields from mid-on.

That brings up the 50 for England, and the 50 partnership between these two, the batsmen meet in the middle and bump gloves together.

Khan to **Quince**, no run, back of a length and wide outside the off stump, the bat flashes at it though there is no contact and it goes through to the keeper.

Khan to **Quince**, wide, similar ball, back of a length but this is swinging away from the batsman and it is left alone outside the off stump. Wide enough for **Umpire du Toit** to put his arms out for a stretch.

Khan to **Quince**, 2 runs, much straighter but also slower at 76mph and easily picked off by Quince as he moves across his stumps in his set up routine and guides it past **Sharma** at midwicket. He does a great job hauling it in and saves what looked like a certain boundary. They only jogged the first one or there could have been 3 there by the time the ball came in.

Khan to **Quince**, no run, great delivery, outswinger starting on off and moving towards 2nd slip. The trigger movement doesn't get him right onto the line of this one as his weight is too far across. The bat is wafted at the ball away from the body, but there is too much swing and it misses everything.

Khan to **Quince**, no run, back to back great deliveries, same outswinging style, back of a length and from off stump out towards the slips. The umpire signals an end to the over. The batsman learns his lesson and shoulders his arms to this one. Good end to the over. While walking up the wicket to meet his partner, **Quince** practises some back foot defensive shots and some 'drop hands' leaves, while muttering to himself.

10:43   "England 53-0 after 9 overs. I think du Toit made a mistake there Bobby, we were a ball short? Did he forget that he gave a wide in the middle of the over? Anyway we have to go with the umpire, and he is already standing at square leg, so he obviously wants that over to be finished. That over also brought up the first 50 runs for England and the 50 run partnership. Ray can you tell us about it."

"Hi Pat, Bobby, England are off to a really good start here, just what they wanted from these two. They are currently going at just a hair under 6 an over. The 50 partnership came in 52 balls, with Rhodes getting 27, Quince getting 20 and 3 wides. There have been 10 doubles, 2 sixes and the rest in singles. Surprisingly no boundaries along the floor yet, although there has been some good chase down fielding. Perhaps they have over- watered that area at the bottom of the slope as it is really slow coming off the square down there. In my opinion they can push on from here as they have a good enough base. If they continue at sixes they will get up to 299, though if they can increase the rate to 7 or 8 then they may get up to 380! A score from the good old days! They don't need any heroics just yet, just keep knocking it around and let the scoreboard turn over. Obviously Pooran has been expensive this morning, though Khan is bowling quite nicely, currently 26 of his 5 overs, an economy rate of 5.2. They need a breakthrough and soon if they are going to stop a big score."

Panda to **Rhodes**, 1 run, off stump line with no spin, pushed out slowly to **Sharma** at mid-off and a stroll single.

Panda to **Quince**, 2 runs, over-pitched outside the off stump and driven sharply through the covers. **Kapoor** running across and diving to his left gets a hand on it, though it can only ricochet down the slope towards the boundary. He is able to recover and pick up the ball which stops the batsmen turning for a third. His rifle arm puts the ball over the stumps after one bounce and into the keeper's gloves.

Panda to **Quince**, no run, big **appeal** from everyone around the batsman as the ball pitches on middle and turns past the bat into the middle of the pad. They are screaming at **Umpire Randall** with their arms in the air and after a moment of contemplation he forcefully shakes his head. They have 15 seconds if they want to review this. After **Sharma** discusses with **Panda** and **Singh,** they decide not to review. Maybe there was a sound on bat, or it was going down leg?

Panda to **Quince**, 1 run, pressure released, ball on middle, back of a length with no spin, slapped down into the ground just pass a terrified short leg, and out to the **Trahar** on the square leg boundary, and the jog through for 1.

Panda to **Rhodes**, 2 runs, similar ball but slower and picked up early, driven off his legs out past midwicket to the boundary, cut off from the rope by a big slide from **Trahar**, an easy 2 as the throw comes in waywardly to the bowler's end.

Panda to **Rhodes**, no run, on line and back of a length, defended back to the bowler.

10:47 "England 59-0 after 10 overs. We have the replay from the LBW appeal coming through, which was given 'not out' and not reviewed. First we go to the HotSpot. Quince has a small stride forward after that shuffle, rocking and rolling the frames, there is nothing on the bat, no contact. Ok let's have a look at the ball tracking, pitches on middle, playing a shot, impact in line, wickets missing! Correct decision from Randall, missing down the leg side with the spin. Well done sir. That brings an end to the first powerplay and the first 10 overs of the match. For the next period, overs 11 to 40 the fielding team is allowed a maximum of 4 fielders outside the 30 yard circle. Bobby, your thoughts on how India are doing and what strategically do they need to change?"

"I don't think they should spread men all over the ground if that's what you mean. They need wickets to try and create some excitement and get some momentum back from England. They have to keep the pressure up even if they leak a few more runs. England will be pleased with the position that they are in, and the method they have gone about getting it. There were 2 big shots, off bad balls, and the rest has been along the ground and safe. They are bringing Mopal on from Azer's end now? That will give him time to get back his energy before the death bowling that he is so famous for. So I say: 'keep the field in tight and trust your bowlers to get wickets.'"

Mopal to **Quince**, 1 run, on the pads as he moves across the stumps and easily guided down to fine leg. Jogging through and settling for one, when they could have tested **Khan's** arm for the second.

"That's right, Varun Mopal has come on from the pavilion end, Bobby. The field looks pretty similar to Khan's set up, though they have pushed the straight men back. So we have 4 on the ropes straight away, wide 3rd man, wide fine leg, deep mid-on and mid-off. Sharma wants to stay close to the action so he has swapped into an short extra cover position. Overall still quite protected on the offside."

Mopal to **Rhodes**, no run, better ball outside the off stump and is watched by and into the keeper's gloves. Not much movement.

Mopal to **Rhodes**, 6 runs, the respect didn't last long, short and on middle stump, medium pace at 78mph and inviting the batsman to pull into the stands. The opportunity is taken and lifted with the pace on the ball over backward square leg and into the Mound Stand. That is the long part of the ground and still he gets the ball 5 rows back. And its caught in the stands! Well done, that man, give us a wave.

Mopal to **Rhodes**, no run, outside off stump seaming away from the right hander and left alone.

Mopal to **Rhodes**, 1 run, on the pads on a good length and defended resolutely up to **Pooran** in front of the Lord's members at deep mid-on and a single is walked.

Mopal to **Quince**, no run, straight ball, around 80mph, on a good length and defended back to the bowler with a full face of the bat.

10:52   England 67-0 after 11 overs. "A really big over for England there and a harsh welcome to the game for Mopal. All that running around in the field he did earlier must have taken its toll. Rhodes just helped the ball on its way to the stands, as if it was a fly he was waving out of the way. He has played nicely so far and is on 37."

Panda to **Rhodes**, no run, there was some turn there! The ball hit something and spat out right, from off stump onto middle. It's played off the back foot defensively and picked up by **Kumar** at short leg.

"The field is a bit more spread out for Panda now that the restrictions have lifted but they are still trying to be aggressive. mid-off pushed back to the rope and there is a sweeper on the offside boundary, to go along with the deep mid-on and deep square leg that were already in place. The silly point has come out and Sharma is coordinating proceedings from short cover. He is waving at deep square leg to try and push him around to a sweeper role on that short boundary."

Panda to **Rhodes**, no run, the attempted doosra, ball pitches on middle though just goes on straight and can be pushed out on the legside where **Pooran** slowly bends down and picks it up at his ankles.

Panda to **Rhodes, caught,** finally the breakthrough comes. Flighted delivery on off stump, the batsmen thinks it is going to turn to leg, but it goes straight on and pops up off the leading edge of the bat, as he tries to play across it to square leg, straight into **Panda's** hands. The batsman shakes his head, rehearses the straight bat defensive shot, but it's too little too late and he turns and starts the long walk back home, while the Indians congratulate each other in the middle of the square.

10:54

| Tom Rhodes | c. & b. Panda | 37 off 40 balls | FOW: 67-1 |

"Brilliant variation from Panda there, built the pressure up and got the batsman playing across the line. Simple catch and you can see what it means to him, Patty; he took off towards the square leg umpire in celebration after he had thrown the ball high into the air on a sort of victory lap. This could be the reset that India needed to change this game. The Indian crowd have suddenly woken up! You could barely hear them five minutes ago, but now you can't hear anything but them!"

"Next out of the hutch is Greg Hanson, promoted up the order today to 3 ahead of Rick Barnes. He has a quick chat with Rhodes as they pass in front of the pavilion and asks Umpire Randall for a middle and leg guard. He is having a look around the ground to the field settings, which has reverted to an aggressive stance once again for him. Silly point back in, and mid-off and mid-on inside the circle. So the only deep men are the sweepers on both side. Here we go Bobby, I'm excited!"

Panda to **Hanson**, 2 runs, full pitch on the off stump, driven firmly back past the bowler towards the Media Centre, it's a long way to reach the boundary and the ball is hauled in by **Mopal**, who flicks it to **Sharma** to complete the throw. They run the first very hard, so the second is a jog through.

Panda to **Hanson**, 2 runs, yorker length on leg stump, played as a half-volley away past midwicket towards cow corner. **Trahar** swoops around from deep square leg to cut it off from the fence though there is another easy 2. **Sharma** is swearing at himself as he wanted **Trahar** to be a little further round which would have saved a run.

Panda to **Hanson**, **appeal stumped**, beautiful delivery floated outside the off stump and a sharp turn towards the stumps. **Hanson** goes for a big drive just as it pitches and plays all around it, through the gate and into the keeper's gloves. **Singh** has the bails off in a flash and appeals to **Umpire du Toit** with an outstretched gloved index finger. **Du Toit** has to go upstairs to check and signals a big square box to our 3rd umpire **Antonio Shivanagale**, from Sri Lanka. The umpire is not convinced though and the soft signal is not-out.

"Umpire to TV director, we have an umpire review for stumping, please can we please check the no-ball line first. Ok it's a legitimate delivery, well inside the line. Now the side on view, ok the ball is through now, into the keeper's hands, and the bails are off now. Please can we rock and roll that moment? Please can we zoom in on the batsman's right foot, ok there, roll it, roll it, back now, ... ok. Thanks. I am ready to make my decision. Umpire du Toit, I need you to reverse your decision please: it is OUT."

10:58

Greg Hanson	st. Singh b. Panda	4 off 3 balls	FOW: 71-2

"Bobby, it's incredible how a game can change in a couple of balls?! This is why we love this sport, it is one way traffic until you get slapped back to reality."

"I told you Patty, after you get the first wicket they can topple very quickly. Hanson was coming into this game on form, and those first two shots looked full of confidence. But then you take a little more risk, go for a daring shot and the game can turn. This is now very much up for grabs. The crowd are going crazy, they sense something special happening, and India have the momentum behind them. I can't believe it, but the producer is telling me that my time here is up, just when the action was getting good, when we come back, you will have Jon alongside you Patty."

10:45 **Vikas @V4India:** @dizzydora @PPringles England can't get up to 380! That's crazy talk. They have been lucky, and Pooran has been rubbish. @dizzydora obviously they need a breakthrough! Thanks for nothing.

10:47 **kiks @nikita_aol:** @PPringles @abirdman that LBW must have been out! It was a glorious delivery. Quince steps across in his set up and covers all of his stumps. How does he not get LBW more often?

10:47 **Andy @abirdman:** *replying to* @nikita_aol nope, going down leg, too much turn. Maybe the impact will be inline? I'm surprised it hit his pads at all. Normally he picks off anything that strays onto his pads.

10:50 **Vikas @V4India:** @Jungan_Official You tell them! They need to stay aggressive. Keep the fielders in and take wickets. The boys can easily make up any cheap runs with some big hitting!

10:51 **Vikas @V4India:** @PPringles @Jungan_Official Where have all the India fans gone? We need our drummers! Show some passion! Jaya Haiiiii! Jaya Haiiiii, Jaya Haiiiii, Jaya Jaya Jaya Jaya Haiiiii.

10:51 **Craig @barmy1992:** *replying to* @V4India Switch to the bright side my friend! Come and have a party with us! Glory Glory Quince and Roadsy, Glory Glory Quince and Roadsy!

10:52 **Geoff @barmyGeoff:** *replying to* @barmy1992 Who is this Mopal geezer? Looks like he is out of Sunday league cricket. More catching practise in the Mound stand! Heads up out there boys! Let me hear that #barmytrumpet!!

10:54   **Vikas @V4India:** @PPringles @Jungan_Official BOOM!! We are back. Bye Bye Rhodes! See you next time! Oh, now you are waking up India??

10:54   **toby @Tobytools:** @PPringles @SirJon cheap ass way to give away your wicket. Watch the ball and hit it. It's an easy game. Is he on the take?

10:55   **Pri   @pinkyofficial:**   @Jungan_Official   WooHoo! @CaptainSharma is back in it! Love you babe! Bring it home! #love #ENGIND #chakdeIndia #lordslife #pimmsoclock

10:56   **toby @Tobytools:** @PPringles @SirJon how much did @LevantePvtInd and @pinkyofficial pay these guy to throw the game?? #fixed

10:58   **Vikas @V4India:** @PPringles @Jungan_Official OMG it has just gone crazy in the Grandstand! That's out! I can see from here umps! No need for the replay! What a take from the turbanator, lightning behind the stumps.

10:59   **toby @Tobytools:** @SirJon @abirdman England collapse again!! Same old England. #fixed by @LevantePvtInd

10:59   **Vikas @V4India:** @PPringles can't hear much singing from @barmy1992 and @barmyGeoff anymore?! Panda got your tongues boys? Haha #gamechanger

10:59   **kiks @nikita_aol:** @PPringles @Jungan_Official It's out! Shivangale overturns the decision! Who would have thought a Sri Lankan would help out India! Incredible over from @GreatWhitePanda! #marryme #hero

11:00   **Jon Knight @SirJon:** *@PPringles* Oh dear, oh dear, oh dear!

CHAPTER 3
ENGLAND 71–2, INDIA YET TO BAT

11:00   "Welcome back into the studio, Jon, and what a time to come in here! England were cruising through the first hour of play, taking no real risks and punishing the bad balls to keep the scorecard ticking over. 10 minutes ago Jones would have been sitting very comfortably at 67 for no loss after 11 overs, half way through their morning cuppas, enjoying the strong English start on this lovely Lord's morning. Now he will be getting his pads on, he may have to come in pretty soon if things get worse! What a change 10 minutes and a fantastic Panda over can make, isn't this why we love cricket?"

"Wow, Patty, just wow. As someone not sitting in that English dressing room right now, I can definitely say this is why I love cricket. The fans in the stadium are going crazy, and it took that first wicket to really wake them up. The blue and orange flags have started waving, the songs and chants are coming from all parts of the ground. They are excited and I'm sure they are loving the action. 10 minutes ago we had given that first hour of play to England, settled opening batsmen in good form, freely scoring to all parts of the ground. Now I would have to say at best its 50-50, probably more in India's hands. Panda has just flipped this game on its head in the matter of an over, and both teams know it. He wasn't even bowling that well in the first two overs, the batsmen picking his variations and knocking the ball around the field for 1s and 2s. I didn't really see anything from him too scary, then in that last over he made it rip! Rhodes was very well settled and will be very disappointed with the shot he played. He should know better than to play across the line like that when the ball is turning even a bit. But you can get those moments of adrenaline in this game which can make you make the wrong choice. They had set an inviting gap on that legside for some easy runs and that gap turned into a trap very quickly. Hanson on the other hand got a ball for the ages. The flight, speed, pitch, turn all absolutely out of the top drawer and would have deceived the best batsmen of the day, let alone someone new to the crease. As a batsman you hope you are able to see it early and be in a defensive mood when that level of ball comes and live to fight another day. But I think Hanson probably came in with too much confidence and that only increased after quickly scoring off his first two balls. In the end some very sharp work from the keeper and he has to make the long walk back."

"Indeed he does Jon, and I'm sure he won't get a warm reception as he walks through the long room or up into the dressing room either? Angus will be annoyed at his short stay at the crease and he is not one to hold his feelings inside! Next up for England is Ricky Barnes who walks through the Long Room, down the pavilion steps and out on the field. He is jogging on the spot a bit and practising his straight drives and pull shots as he dances up towards the square."

"Patty, sorry to interject, but you can see the expressions on the Indian team's faces from up here and the smirks they are giving him as he walks past them. They are almost giddy with excitement!"

"No worries Jon, of course the Indians know Barney very well from his time with the Rangers in Goa. He played there with Mopal and Kumar and his big hitting got them through the playoffs and to the trophy just a few weeks ago. They know he would not have expected to come in this early and they are going to put serious pressure on him. Quince has come down halfway to the pavilion to meet Barney as he walks past the Indian team huddle and to give him some support. These two now have a job to do. That last wicket was at the end of the over so Barney will be at the non-striker's end, and he won't be immediately thrust under the spotlight. It looks like it will be Mopal to continue from the pavilion end bowling towards us. For Quince he has kept a defensive field with the 4 "outside" fielders at fine leg, third man, deep mid-off and deep mid-on."

Mopal to **Quince**, 1 run, straight ball, defended with pace down to deep mid-on for an easy single, fielded by **Pooran.**

"The deep men at mid-on and mid-off have come up for the new batsman, and the midwicket fielder has gone into the slip cordon. They have 2 slips, 3rd man, point, cover, short extra cover, mid-off, mid-on, and fine leg."

Mopal to **Barnes**, 2 runs, on the pads, easy pickings out through the gap at midwicket. **Pooran** has to chase it as it runs down the slope, and the throw is very good to the bowler's end so no chance for a third.

Mopal to **Barnes**, no run, better ball outside the off stump and swinging away. Left alone by the batsman.

Mopal to **Barnes**, 2 runs, short ball only 79 mph, picked up quickly but hit high on the bat going for the pull shot. The ball runs out through square leg and must be fielded by a diving **Khan** from wide fine leg.

Mopal to **Barnes**, no run, good length on the off stump defended out to **Panda** at point.

Mopal to **Barnes**, 2 runs, too full, straight drive past the bowler's outstretched left hand. It's a long boundary back to the pavilion and **Trahar** from mid-off makes the save before the rope and to the applause of the Lord's members, back hands it to a chasing **Pooran** who gets it into the bowler's end.

11:06   England 78-2 after 13 overs. "Well Patty that is the way to take all the pressure off a new incoming batsman. So many opportunities to score and some woeful bowling. Too straight and too full and easy runs coming all around the ground."

"I agree Jon, a very friendly welcome to the game. We have the Indian hero of the first hour continuing from the nursery end."

Panda to **Quince**, no run, outside off stump with little spin left alone by the batsman.

Panda to **Quince**, 2 runs, on the pads and played out behind short midwicket towards the Grandstand. **Trahar** fields from deep square leg, and a wayward throw towards the keeper's end allows the second run to be comfortably taken.

Panda to **Quince**, no run, better delivery, outside off-stump line with some turn to middle, defended solidly.

Panda to **Quince**, 1 bye, good length and line delivery, it kicks off something on the surface, and jumps past the bat and over the keeper's gloves and past him towards the pavilion. **Bihari** chases it down from slip as **Barnes** calls through for an easy single. Keeper, bowler, captain and batsmen all questioning each other where that bounce came from.

Panda to **Barnes**, no run, very good length and line, defended back to the bowler.

Panda to **Barnes**, 1 run, on the pads, tried the doosra but doesn't work and knocked out to deep square leg where **Trahar** fields and gets it more accurately this time back to the keeper.

11:10 England 82-2 after 14 overs. "Over to Ray now for some statistics from Rhodes' innings."

"Thanks Patty, I really need to catch up and catch my breath at the end of that hour. I had started preparing some information of Rhodes's innings just when Hanson lands on my desk too. Rhodes scored 37 runs off 40 balls before being caught. Normally his runs come from all around the wicket, though today 54% of his runs, including those two maximums, came through the midwicket and 24% through the covers. It looks like the short boundary up to the Grandstand and slope down to the Mound Stand are already starting to play an active role in this game, and the long straight boundaries are harder to reach. Hanson's innings obviously didn't really get started so not much to analyse there. While I am at it, I can also give you some info about Khan's first spell? As you know he bowled 5 overs, no maidens, no wickets for 26 runs. He had 2 wides, but the umpire missed an extra ball on one of them, so has only bowled 31 deliveries. 15 dot balls and that 1 maximum when Quince put him into the stands.

61% of his balls so far have been either a good length or just back of a length, which is impressive control, although 22% have been short. 5 balls out of 31, or 16%, have been down leg side which at this level is too high and dangerous. In conclusion, he is bowling well, just needs to find a more consistent line."

Mopal to **Quince**, 1 run, straight line on the pads, solidly defended out to **Pooran** at deep mid-on for a jogged single.

After the last over Sharma is sticking to the defensive field for Barnes too now.

Mopal to **Barnes**, no run, swings at a wide one attempting to smash it through the covers but gets nothing on it. Walks away towards the square leg umpire practising a leave shot.

Mopal to **Barnes**, no run, straight and back of a length, leaves this one alone outside the off stump, with forced high arms. Just as he practised.

Mopal to **Barnes**, 1 run, outside the off stump, but slower and played with soft hands down through gully to **Shubanka** at third man.

Mopal to **Quince**, no run, outswinger outside off stump, left alone by Quince. As he shuffles across his stumps throws his arms and the bat out towards midwicket where they are safe away from the ball.

Mopal to **Quince**, 1 run, too full, driven back past the bowler, though there is cover in front of the pavilion as **Trahar** fields at deep mid-off.

11:15 England 85-2 after 15 overs. "Much better control from Mopal in that last over, and the defensive field gave him lots of protection. Don't expect it will help them take many wickets though and 85 for 2 is a strong platform for England to go on and get a big score."

Panda to **Quince**, 2 runs, middle stump line with some flight and picked up as a half volley out through midwicket towards the Grandstand. **Trahar** runs around and dives before it hits the boundary and get the ball to the bowler's end. They only jogged the first one, thinking it would be 4, so good run-saving from the fielder.

Panda to **Quince**, 2 runs, outside the off stump, yorker length, but played as a full toss, past a terrified silly point out across the square and towards the point boundary. There is cover out there and **Kapoor** runs around from deep extra cover to get the ball into the keeper before they try for the third.

Panda to **Quince**, no run, there's the turn! Lovely flight on the ball outside the off stump and turns towards the batsman on middle. Defended in his crease with a straight bat back to the bowler.

Panda to **Quince**, 2 runs, too much turn this time. On middle and turning down the legside away to leg, there is a small inside edge on the ball and it runs very fine between the keeper and the short fine leg. **Khan** has to chase the ball back up towards the pavilion and isn't that quick chasing it down, so they run through for 2.

Panda to **Quince**, no run, bowler is finding something now in this pitch. Nice flight, turning into the batsman and defended.

Panda to **Quince**, 2 runs, finishes the over with a bad ball, full toss smashed away towards midwicket where **Pooran** makes a diving attempt of a catch to his right. Can only get a hand to the ball and it slows down enough for **Trahar** to come around and cut off the boundary. 50-50 chance but at least stopped a certain boundary.

11:19 England 93-2 after 16 overs. "We will take drinks now. David Wigglesworth and Umesh Sriraj will bring on the drinks for the respective teams and this could be an opportunity for some tactical changes Jon?"

"Yes Pat, the innings is nicely poised with both sides getting their fair chance at it. I wouldn't think the batsmen would want to make any big changes in their styles just yet, we still have 35, no 34, overs to go and so there is still plenty of time. The Indians however will have really been encouraged by the last few overs from Panda. He has been a bit expensive though is getting the ball to grip and turn, even though it is still relatively new, I guess only 8 overs old at that end.

Then to come they have the leg spinner Shubanka who will be able to get even more out of the pitch than Panda. Apart from Khan the Indian quicks haven't been great, though no one was really expecting that they would be. The conditions are not favouring them, and they are not used to bowling on this type of English wicket. I don't think Pooran or Mopal have the guile to make the ball do unusual things when the pitch is offering no help."

"England will be very happy with the rate they are going at?"

"For sure; a shade under 6 per over is fantastic for this stage of the innings. It gives them a solid platform to build on. However the field is more spread out now, Panda and Mopal have shown that they can keep it tight if they need to, and of course those 2 wickets in quick session will have dented their confidence. Rhodes will be telling the boys in the hutch that the pitch is playing flat, though visually they have seen the few surprises that it is spitting out in the last couple of overs, so won't be sitting too comfortably. If these two can build something for the next 15-20 overs, maybe with the loss of 1 wicket, and they can get to that 35th over with 5-6 wickets in hand they will be able to go aggressive and put an unbeatable score on the board."

"Let's go down to Mike who is getting the early thoughts of Sunil Sharma, the Indian captain?"

"Thanks Patty, Jon, yes that's right I just managed to catch hold of the Indian captain here. Sunil, how are you assessing the state of play so far this morning?"

"Mike, I'll be honest it's been a bit of a grind. This was always going to be a batting surface and was going to be an uphill struggle for the bowling team. But I am really proud of the way my boys have come out and done their work so far. Azer and Pooran up front made the ball move around and put the openers under some pressure. For sure there were some loose deliveries but overall they kept it tidy. Then when Panda came on, he tightened the scoring rate up even further, and got those 2 important break throughs, which gave us a real boost. Rhodes and Hanson are both dangerous batsman so it's good they can't impact the score anymore. At the start of the innings I would have taken a score under 100, with a few wickets, after 16 overs. We are not too far off that, so I can't be disappointed."

"We saw you having a jib at Barney as he came into bat? What was going on there?"

"Haha, nothing, it was all friendly. Just putting him under some pressure up front. Given the way England were going he wouldn't have expected to be out here so early, we were just reminding him of that. Mopal and Kumar are particularly keen to get stuck into him. They were team mates just a few weeks ago, winning the IPL, but this is a different day. Don't worry we will get him and Quince back in the clubhouse pretty sharpish. This game isn't done yet."

"Thanks Sunil, Patty, I agree with the Indian captain: the game looks nicely balanced so far from down here. We are set for a cracker."

11:20   **Google Search: Goan Rangers IPL 2030**

The Goa Rangers are one of the 10 franchise teams of the *Levante Indian Premier League* cricket tournament. They are the current Champions having won the 2030 season. For more info click here: *crickopedia.co/GoaRangers*
Redirect: *crickopedia.co/IPL2030*

The 2030 season of the Indian Premier League, also known as IPL 22, was the 22nd season of the IPL, a professional domestic Twenty20 cricket tournament created by the Indian Cricket Organisation (ICO), in 2007. This season was held between 5th April and 26th May 2030. The tournament continues to be sponsored by the Levante Group, who acquired the naming rights in 2026 for a period of 10 years, for an undisclosed fee.

Goa Rangers beat Bangalore in the final on Sunday 26th May 2030 to claim their second IPL trophy, having won it before in the 19th edition. The Orange Cap went to Ricky Barnes of the Goa Rangers for the most runs in the tournament, with 812 runs at an average of 45.1. The purple cap, for most wickets taken, went to Umesh Sriraj of Chennai with a total of 46 wickets. Captain of the Goa Rangers, Ravi Kumar, was named most valuable player of the tournament, with a tournament high average of 47, and Sonia Chancellor, appearing in her first IPL tournament and with 32 wickets, was named upcoming player of the year.

Background

<u>Format</u>
This edition featured 10 teams across a shortened 8 week period. This shortened period was agreed by the ICO and the franchise teams after an agreement was struck between the ICO and the BCCE for the Indian National Cricket team to tour England in the summer of 2030, a tour to include one day international, IT20s and test matches. In agreeing to this new format the ICO agreed to increase the salary cap to $100m per team, for a maximum squad size of 30 players, and agreed to pay for the travel costs of the team between matches by private jet. This allowed the teams to play matches in different cities on back to back days, though at the request of the Indian Players Union, this was to be limited as much as possible. The schedule for the tournament was released on 15th November 2029.

The Tournament itself is divided into a Round Robin Group Stage where every team will play each other home and away. 2 points are awarded for a win, 1 point for a tie and no points for a loss. Teams with the same number of points will be ranked based on number of wins away from home. The top 4 teams in the table will then qualify for the play offs.

In the playoffs, Qualifiers 1 and 2 will play each other first, with the winner put straight through to the final. Then qualifiers 3 and 4 will play each other, and the winner will then play the loser of the first Playoff match for a place in the final.

<u>Broadcast and Sponsorship</u>
The 2030 tournament is the first year of a 5-year deal between YouTube and the ICO for the global distribution rights for the tournament. This agreement was signed in 2028, through a rights bidding process. YouTube outbid Star Entertainment and

Amazon for exclusive rights to the broadcasting, for a fee of RCr 96,800 crore ($11 billion), for both the live action and the highlights shows.

The Levante Group won the naming rights to the tournament in a sealed bid auction in 2026 for a period of 10 years. The ICO has lined up 10 other Global ambassador partners for the event and a further 10 advertising sponsors. In total there were 21 corporate sponsors for the 2030 edition.

The total revenue from broadcasting and central sponsorship, which is estimated at RCr 30,000 crore ($3.4 billion) of the tournament each year is split in 3 ways by the ICO. One third is retained by the ICO to fund its ongoing operations alongside investing in grass roots cricket projects across India. A second third is split evenly across all the teams, with each of the 10 teams receiving approximately $100m, and the final third being allocated to the teams in order of their finishing position in the table.

In 2030 for winning the tournament the Goa Rangers received a total pay-out from the ICO of approximately $320 million.

Players

The players were chosen from a player auction which took place between 5-10 January 2030. Each team was allowed a maximum of 6 overseas players in their squads of which the gameday 11 could only have a maximum of 4 overseas players.

None of the captains of the franchises locked from the 2029 tournament were available to be auctioned and each will receive a salary of 10% higher than the maximum auctioned player.

The captains of the franchises are:

Franchise	Player	Nationality
Bangalore	Tom Rhodes	England
Chennai	Ankit Bihari	India
Delhi	Rohan Kapoor	India
Goa	Ravi Kumar	India
Hyderabad	William Jones	England
Jaipur	Azer Khan	India

Kolkata	Cameron Spencer	West Indies
Mohali	Shawn Lock	Australia
Mumbai	Sunil Sharma	India
Pune	Mitch Williams	Australia

In the 2030 auction Nikil Panda received the highest auction bid, with Mohali offering him $5m for the tournament. The highest overseas played was English all-rounder Patrick Sherman who was offered $4.3m by Jaipur. A notable mention, Sonia Chancellor, the first female player in the IPL, was won at auction by Mumbai for $2.6m.

The Group Stage

The League Table

		Played	Win	Loss	Tie	Points	Home win	Away win	Bat first	Bowl First
Q1	Chennai	18	12	5	1	25	8	4	6	6
Q2	Goa	18	12	6		24	6	6	5	7
Q3	Pune	18	11	6	1	23	5	6	6	5
Q4	Bangalore	18	11	7		22	7	4	7	4
	Hyderabad	18	10	8		20	7	3	5	5
	Mumbai	18	7	11		14	3	4	5	2
	Jaipur	18	7	11		14	5	2	6	1
	Kolkata	18	7	11		14	6	1	4	3
	Mohali	18	6	12		12	3	3	4	2
	Delhi	18	6	12		12	4	2	4	2

The League Progression

Game	1	2	3	4	5	6	7	8	9	10	11	12	13	14	15	16	17	18
Bangalore	2	4	4	6	8	8	8	10	12	14	16	16	16	16	18	20	22	22
Chennai	2	4	4	4	6	8	10	12	13	13	13	15	17	19	19	21	23	25
Delhi	0	0	2	4	6	6	6	6	8	8	8	8	10	12	12	12	12	12
Goa	0	2	2	4	6	8	8	8	8	10	12	14	16	16	18	20	22	24
Hyderabad	2	2	4	4	6	8	8	8	10	12	12	12	12	14	14	16	18	20
Jaipur	2	2	2	2	2	4	4	6	6	6	6	8	10	12	12	12	12	14
Kolkata	0	0	2	2	2	2	4	4	4	6	8	10	12	14	14	14	14	14
Mohali	0	0	0	2	2	4	6	8	10	10	10	10	10	10	10	10	12	12
Mumbai	0	2	4	4	4	4	6	6	6	6	8	10	10	10	12	12	14	14
Pune	2	4	6	8	8	8	10	12	13	15	17	17	17	19	19	21	23	23

The Match Summary

Away

Home \ Away	Bangalore	Chennai	Delhi	Goa	Hyderabad	Jaipur	Kolkata	Mohali	Mumbai	Pune
Bangalore	x	Bangalore 25 runs	Bangalore 6 wickets	Goa 1 wicket	Bangalore 3 runs	Bangalore 5 wickets	Bangalore 33 runs	Mohali 6 runs	Bangalore 10 wickets	Bangalore 18 runs
Chennai	Chennai 7 wickets	x	Chennai 9 wickets	Chennai 17 runs	Chennai 2 wickets	Chennai 15 runs	Chennai 35 runs	Chennai 28 runs	Mumbai 22 runs	Chennai 6 wickets
Delhi	Bangalore 14 runs	Chennai 4 wickets	x	Delhi 27 runs	Delhi 18 runs	Delhi 12 runs	Delhi 8 runs	Mohali 5 wickets	Mumbai 15 runs	Pune 32 runs
Goa	Goa 6 wickets	Goa 48 runs	Delhi 2 wickets	x	Hyderabad 5 wickets	Goa 8 wickets	Goa 25 runs	Goa 13 runs	Mumbai 16 runs	Goa 3 runs
Hyderabad	Hyderabad 18 runs	Hyderabad 7 wickets	Hyderabad 3 wickets	Hyderabad 7 runs	x	Hyderabad 15 runs	Hyderabad 20 runs	Mohali 10 runs	Hyderabad 6 wickets	Pune 10 runs
Jaipur	Bangalore 17 runs	Chennai 3 wickets	Jaipur 19 runs	Goa 62 runs	Jaipur 2 runs	x	Jaipur 4 wickets	Jaipur 11 runs	Jaipur 10 runs	Pune 8 wickets
Kolkata	Kolkata 3 wickets	Kolkata 4 runs	Delhi 6 wickets	Goa 6 wickets	Kolkata 5 wickets	Kolkata 8 runs	x	Kolkata 18 runs	Kolkata 3 wickets	Pune 3 wickets
Mohali	Bangalore 52 runs	Chennai 5 runs	Mohali 18 runs	Goa 7 wickets	Mohali 5 wickets	Jaipur 32 runs	Mohali 9 runs	x	Mumbai 8 wickets	Pune 5 runs
Mumbai	Bangalore 6 wickets	Chennai 17 runs	Mumbai 3 runs	Goa 8 wickets	Hyderabad 4 wickets	Jaipur 15 runs	Mumbai 2 runs	Mumbai 3 wickets	x	Pune 22 runs
Pune	Pune 5 wickets	Tie	Pune 10 wickets	Goa 1 wicket	Hyderabad 2 runs	Pune 16 runs	Kolkata 6 runs	Pune 10 runs	Pune 2 wickets	x

Home

The <u>Match Results</u>

	Game 1				Game 2				Game 3			
	Home	Away	Winner	How	Home	Away	Winner	How	Home	Away	Winner	How
5th April	Mumbai	Jaipur	Jaipur	15 run								
6th April	Bangalore	Delhi	Bangalore	6 wickets	Chennai	Kolkata	Chennai	35 runs				
7th April	Goa	Hyderabad	Hyderabad	5 wickets	Mohali	Pune	Pune	5 runs				
8th April	Jaipur	Chennai	Chennai	3 wickets	Mumbai	Delhi	Mumbai	3 runs				
9th April	Kolkata	Goa	Goa	6 wickets	Mohali	Bangalore	Bangalore	52 runs				
10th April	Hyderabad	Pune	Pune	10 runs								
11th April	Chennai	Mumbai	Mumbai	22 runs	Kolkata	Mohali	Kolkata	18 runs				
12th April	Pune	Bangalore	Pune	5 wickets	Delhi	Jaipur	Delhi	12 runs				
13th April	Hyderabad	Goa	Hyderabad	7 runs								

	Game 1				Game 2				Game 3		
14th April	Hyderabad	Mohali	Mohali	10 runs	Pune	Jaipur	Pune	16 runs			
15th April	Mumbai	Goa	Goa	8 wickets	Delhi	Kolkata	Delhi	8 runs			
16th April	Bangalore	Chennai	Bangalore	25 runs	Pune	Hyderabad	Hyderabad	2 runs			
17th April	Kolkata	Delhi	Delhi	6 wickets	Goa	Jaipur	Goa	8 wickets			
18th April	Mohali	Chennai	Chennai	5 runs	Bangalore	Mumbai	Bangalore	10 wickets			
19th April	Hyderabad	Delhi	Hyderabad	3 wickets	Goa	Pune	Goa	3 runs			
20th April	Bangalore	Mohali	Mohali	6 runs	Jaipur	Kolkata	Jaipur	4 wickets			
21st April	Delhi	Pune	Pune	32 runs	Mumbai	Chennai	Chennai	17 runs			
22nd April											
23rd April	Kolkata	Bangalore	Kolkata	3 wickets	Goa	Mumbai	Mumbai	16 runs			
24th April	Chennai	Jaipur	Chennai	15 runs	Mohali	Hyderabad	Mohali	5 wickets			

Date	Game 1				Game 2				Game 3			
25th April	Mumbai	Pune	Pune	22 runs	Delhi	Bangalore	Bangalore	14 runs				
26th April	Chennai	Goa	Chennai	17 runs	Jaipur	Hyderabad	Jaipur	2 runs				
27th April	Mohali	Kolkata	Mohali	9 runs	Delhi	Goa	Delhi	27 runs				
28th April	Mumbai	Bangalore	Bangalore	6 wickets	Hyderabad	Jaipur	Hyderabad	15 runs				
29th April	Pune	Chennai	Tie		Goa	Kolkata	Goa	25 runs				
30th April	Delhi	Mohali	Mohali	5 wickets	Jaipur	Bangalore	Bangalore	17 runs				
1st May	Hyderabad	Chennai	Hyderabad	7 wickets	Pune	Mumbai	Pune	2 wickets				
2nd May	Kolkata	Jaipur	Kolkata	8 runs	Mohali	Goa	Goa	7 wickets				
3rd May	Bangalore	Hyderabad	Bangalore	3 runs	Kolkata	Chennai	Kolkata	4 runs				
4th May	Pune	Delhi	Pune	10 wickets	Mohali	Mumbai	Mumbai	8 wickets				
5th May	Goa	Bangalore	Goa	6 wickets	Chennai	Hyderabad	Chennai	2 wickets	Mohali	Jaipur	Jaipur	32 runs

	Game 1				Game 2				Game 3			
6th May	Delhi	Mumbai	Mumbai	15 runs	Pune	Kolkata	Kolkata	6 runs				
7th May	Chennai	Bangalore	Chennai	7 wickets	Jaipur	Mumbai	Jaipur	10 runs				
8th May	Pune	Goa	Goa	1 wicket	Delhi	Hyderabad	Delhi	18 runs				
9th May	Kolkata	Mumbai	Kolkata	3 wickets	Chennai	Mohali	Chennai	28 runs				
10th May	Hyderabad	Bangalore	Hyderabad	18 runs	Goa	Delhi	Delhi	2 wickets				
11th May	Pune	Mohali	Pune	10 runs	Kolkata	Hyderabad	Kolkata	5 wickets	Goa	Chennai	Goa	48 runs
12th May	Jaipur	Delhi	Bangalore	19 runs	Bangalore	Pune	Bangalore	18 runs				
13th May	Mumbai	Mohali	Chennai	3 wickets	Chennai	Delhi	Chennai	9 wickets				
14th May	Bangalore	Jaipur	Kolkata	5 wickets	Pune	Pune	Pune	3 wickets				
15th May	Hyderabad	Kolkata	Hyderabad	20 runs	Goa	Mohali	Goa	13 runs				
16th May												

	Game 1				Game 2				Game 3			
17th May	Jaipur	Pune	Pune	8 wickets	Hyderabad	Mumbai	Hyderabad	6 wickets	Mohali	Delhi	Mohali	18 runs
18th May	Mumbai	Kolkata	Mumbai	2 runs	Jaipur	Goa	Goa	62 runs	Delhi	Chennai	Chennai	4 wickets
19th May	Bangalore	Kolkata	Bangalore	33 runs	Mumbai	Hyderabad	Hyderabad	4 wickets				
20th May	Bangalore	Goa	Goa	1 wicket	Jaipur	Mohali	Jaipur	11 runs	Chennai	Pune	Chennai	6 wickets

The Playoffs

Preliminary

22nd May 2030 - 12pm - Chennai				24th May 2030 - 6pm - Chennai		
1	Chennai	150	18.2 overs			
2	Goa	166/4	20 overs	Chennai	163/8	20 overs
				Bangalore	178/9	20 overs
22nd May 2030 - 6pm - Pune						
3	Pune	139/7	20 overs			
4	Bangalore	140/6	17.3 overs			

Final

26th May 2030 - 2pm - Mumbai		
Goa	157/4	19.1 overs
Bangalore	155/6	20 overs

*Goa won the toss and elected to field

Special Awards

Winning Team	Goa Rangers
Winning Captain	Ravi Kumar (Goa)
Orange Cap (most runs)	Ricky Barnes (Goa)
Purple Cap (most wickets)	Umesh Sriraj (Chennai)
MVP	Ravi Kumar (Goa)
Upcoming Player	Sonia Chancellor (Mumbai)
Coke Perfect Catch	SK Trahar (Kolkata)
Levante Most Stylish	Sonia Chancellor (Mumbai)
Fair play Award	Pune

11:25   England 93-2 after 16 overs.

Mopal to **Barnes**, 1 run, straight ball solidly defended down to deep mid-off where **Trahar** fields.

Mopal to **Quince**, no run, back of a length defended out to point off the back foot.

Mopal to **Quince**, no run, back of a length and swinging away towards the slips, left alone.

Mopal to **Quince**, 1 run, on middle though full, defended with the bat in front of the pads down to deep long-on where **Pooran** fields.

Mopal to **Barnes**, 1 run, on leg side and short, fended off the chest and the balls runs down to **Khan** at fine leg.

Mopal to **Quince**, no run, left alone with raised arms outside the off stump and through to the keeper.

11:30   England 96-2 after 17 overs. "Hiya Andy, welcome back to the studio, having a good morning so far?"

"Hey Patty, yes really enjoying the cricket so far and England have gotten themselves into a strong position, so that's good too. The view from up here in the media centre is fantastic isn't it! You can't quite see the expressions on their faces, but you can see the movement of the ball, the field placings and you can sort of work out the strategy that the Indians are employing. Much easier from up here than in the middle for sure. Mopal had a great over there too, got through it quickly without giving anything away. I think we are going to get a change at this end? Shubanka the other spinner is coming on."

"Yes, it looks like he will be taking over from Panda at the Nursery end. Sharma is giving the leg spinner a pretty orthodox field. Deep men in the covers and over square leg, and 2 deep men at mid-on and -off. So boundary cover in front of the wicket, but 3rd man and fine leg brought into the circle. The field was very aggressive for Panda after he took those 2 wickets, with a slip, silly point and short leg, but this looks defensive. They are losing the men under the nose of the batsman for the leg spinner. So, going around the ground, we have short 3rd man and short fine leg, slip, short extra cover, sweepers on both sides, midwicket and finally 2 men on the boundary either side of the Media Centre just down in front of us. Barnes has taken his time to survey the field and has asked for a leg stump guard."

Shubanka to **Barnes**, 2 runs, very loose first delivery short and down leg side with not a lot of spin, comes down the track and drives it past midwicket and **Kumar** from deep mid-on has to run around to field it with a dive. Barnes would have wanted a boundary there, easy pickings, but good fielding.

Shubanka to **Barnes**, no run, better, flight on the ball, pitching on middle and knocked down to **Panda** at midwicket.

Shubanka to **Barnes**, no run, on the off stump and turning away, left alone by the batsman.

Shubanka to **Barnes**, **appeal** for LBW, they all go up screaming at **Umpire Randall**. Bowler, keeper, slip, short cover, midwicket, all holding their hands aloft. And he has given it **OUT**. The batsman can't believe it and immediately walks down towards his batting partner complaining towards the umpire. He thinks he hit it? They are going to **review**! **Umpire Randall** makes the TV signal to **Umpire Shivangale** somewhere in the stands around the ground.

"TV director, please, we have a batsman's review for LBW. The on-field decision is out. First can you please show me the bowler's foot? Ok yes that is a legal delivery. Now the front on view please. Ball is in the air, pitching and going on to hit the pads just below the knee rolls as the bat comes across. It doesn't seem like any contact. Can you please rock and roll it for me. Ok, ball passing the bat now, and then onto the pads. Please can I have Snicko up? Ok, ball passing now, oh there is a noise on the monitor. Is that the bat hitting the ground, or perhaps his foot? Can you please show me the hot spot on this angle? Ok ball passing again, slowly, slowly, … YES there is a mark. There is a mark on the inside edge of the bat and on the ball. Ok please put Umpire Randall back on the screen. Theodore, I need you to reverse your decision please. It is NOT OUT."

Shubanka to **Barnes**, 1 run, fuller delivery driven softly down to **Kumar** at deep mid-on.

Shubanka to **Quince**, no run, pitching on middle with some flight and turn to off stump, defended with a full faced bat back to the bowler.

11:35   England 99-2 after 18 overs. "Patty: what a break Barney got there. He was adamant he hit it. You could see his face get red with anger as he marched down to Quince at the other end. It didn't look like Quince really agreed with him though and they used almost all of the time they had to make a decision discussing it. They only get the one review in one-dayers so they can be game-changing. But in the end, you can't argue with Barney when he looks like he is about to punch you, and he was right!"

"Andy, that mark on the bat was so small I'm not sure how Barnes even knew he had hit it? There were a couple of sounds and the bat hit his foot at the same sort of time so would have been very tough call. The umpire must have been convinced or he would have given the benefit of the doubt to the batsman, as a soft call."

"As a batsman if you've hit it, you know. You feel it in your fingers, however thick your gloves are or how heavy the bat is. But – that works both ways – if you get a sneaky edge on a caught behind you also know! No one walks in professional cricket anymore so the acting that comes after that is purely for luck – leave the call up to the umpire to send you on your way, or not!"

Mopal to **Barnes**, 2 runs, offline short delivery pulled, but off the top of the bat, behind square leg. There is not much cover on that side and **Khan** has to field from fine leg. Bit of a mishit means it would not have reached the boundary down the slope and so they run hard for 2. 100 up for England and the batsman bump fists in the middle as a muted celebration.

Mopal to **Barnes**, no run, back of a length and outside off stump. Left alone with arms above shoulders just to make sure.

Mopal to **Barnes**, 2 runs, middle and leg line, back of a length, clipped off the pads down to **Khan** at fine leg, who makes an absolute meal of the fielding, tries to get down to the ball but hits his foot and runs another 10m away horizontally. They ran the first one hard and take a risky second on the mis-field. Could have been a chance if the throw had been better. The bowler is furious.

Mopal to **Barnes**, 2 runs, outside off stump and too full, lovely flowing cover-drive half- volley. **Kapoor** does some lovely work in the covers to get a hand to it to slow down a certain boundary. **Panda** chases after it from point and gets it back in. **Mopal** stood his ground on the left of the pitch and **Barnes** almost knocks him over while running with his head down. They are mouthing something at each other, and lots of pointing going on. It's getting heated, and **Umpire du Toit** has to step in settle everyone down.

Mopal to **Barnes**, no run, short angry bouncer, ducked under by the batsman. Maybe a no ball? Was one of his quickest deliveries so far at 88mph. Wry smile from the batsman back to **Mopal** who is scowling.

Mopal to **Barnes**, 2 runs, another short ball picked early and pulled at, but without much composure and hit high on the bat looping high into the air. A chance for a catch over the head of **Kumar** running backwards at midwicket but it is out of reach for him and the ball loses all speed as it hits the ground. Collected and delivered back to the keeper quickly.

11:40 England 107-2 after 19 overs. "Andy it's all kicking off now?"

"Haha, this is what we pay to see, and why I got out while I still could. Mopal was really firing some dangerous shots at Barney in those last few balls, but in the end all he has to show for it is an amused batsman and an expensive over. You have to be able to hold your nerve in these matches, especially when mistakes start to creep in. I have no idea what sport Khan thought he was playing with that fielding though lets be honest he is at fine leg because they don't think he can field much! Its up to the bowler then to put those mistakes behind him for the team and keep it tight. There was a catch chance, but apart from that nothing in that over will impress the captain."

Shubanka to **Quince**, 2 runs, dancing up the pitch to meet the short ball and clipped off the pads through the gap between midwicket and deep mid-on. **Kumar** runs around to field it and **Panda** chasing from midwicket cannons it into the keeper's end to stop the third run.

Shubanka to **Quince**, 1 run, fuller delivery on the pads and driven down to **Kumar** for an easy single.

Shubanka to **Barnes**, 2 runs, batsman charges the bowler and it is delivered short and driven straight back towards him, where he can just get a hand on it to slow it down and it trickles down towards the media centre for **Khan** to run in from the offside to field it. They know they can target **Khan** for an easy 2, and **Quince** is quickly back to the bowler's end.

Shubanka to **Barnes**, no run, full and outside the off stump. Left alone by the batsman as the fielding team exclaim how close it was with hands on their heads. **Sharma** runs up to the bowler to give him an encouraging pat on the bum.

Shubanka to **Barnes**, 1 run, short ball hit up in the air square of the wicket, drops in front of the **Trahar** the legside sweeper, who protects the boundary, rather than attempting a diving catch.

Shubanka to **Quince**, 4 runs, short ball picked early and dispatched with one bounce over cow corner. **Trahar** had no chance at stopping this one and the steward throws him back the ball.

11:44   England 117-2 after 20 overs. "These two batsmen are starting to find their ranges and their groove now. That is 18 runs off the last 2 overs, with that last shot being the first 4 of the match. The bowlers are letting England get in here, Andy?"

"That was not a great over. Too short from Shubanka and it was only a matter of time before the batsmen got their angles right and started to put the ball away. Both spinners are bowling with that short leg side boundary out to the Grandstand too, which is a big risk, but the quicks want the slope's help into the right-handers. Talking about them, Mopal is looking really tired. I think you were discussing it at the top of the programme? He put in a lot of overs into the IPL just a few weeks ago, and I don't think he has recovered from the Goan party hangover yet. They should probably have gone with Umesh in that slot, but they wanted English experience, which Mopal has from Leeds last year. Now after 5 overs it is showing – and in fact they are taking him off. Pooran is coming back but this time from the pavilion end."

Pooran to **Barnes**, 1 run, on the pads first up and defended solidly down to **Mopal** at deep mid-on.

Pooran to **Quince**, 2 runs, full on off stump, driven through the covers up the hill towards the Grandstand. **Sharma** has to turn and chase it from short extra cover.

Pooran to **Quince**, no run, better ball, on a good line and length, moving inwards, though left alone by the batsmen and it bounces over off stump.

Pooran to **Quince**, wide, tries to straighten up his line though adjust too much and push it down the leg side. **Quince** continues his trigger walk across to the off stump and lets it pass him down the legside. Good take by the diving keeper to stop more runs.

Pooran to **Quince**, no run, offside line moving into the batsman, defended on the back foot with his full body behind the ball.

Pooran to **Quince**, 1 run, outside off, guided down to **Shubanka** at 3rd man with an open face of the bat. That's 50 up for Quince off 59 balls. He runs past the bowler's end and takes his helmet off and holds his bat and arms high in the air to receive a standing ovation from the Lord's crowd. The batsmen share a celebratory embrace before getting back to their marks and continuing with the jobs at hand. The English fans finally have something good to celebrate and are enjoying themselves loudly.

Pooran to **Barnes, caught**, reverses the swing direction and gets the ball to move away from the batsman, who tries to get the bat out of the way though gets a thin outside edge and it flies quickly to **Bihari** at a wide 1st slip who takes it with upturned hands in front of his nose. The crowd are stunned into silence, until the Indian contingent take over.

11:50

| Ricky Barnes | c. Bihari | 25 of 25 balls | FOW: 122-3 |
| | b. Pooran | | |

11:52 England 122-3 after 21 overs. "The change of bowler does it for them, Patty! Another rollercoaster of emotions for the crowd. I was thinking for a few minutes there that this was going to be same old Pooran, get knocked around for some runs, bowl some wides, and get taken off after a few overs. But he gets the breakthrough that India needed. What a rollercoaster the crowd had at the end of that over. Not much happening, then Quince gets his 50 and they give him the ovation that he richly deserves. That gives the Barmy army back some of their voice and the trumpets start blazing out again. 2 mins later they get the wind knocked out of them and the Indian fans go crazy. Nothing gets the emotions racing all over the place like live sport."

"Indeed, Andy, and it will be the England captain next out of the hutch I think, just when they need to him to come and steady the ship? Wait, I think we are getting a change in the batting order here. I am just getting word that Sam King has been promoted up from seven, ahead of Bill Jones and Patrick Sherman to come in at five. Wow that's interesting news, lots of pressure on the debutant, Andy?"

"If it is true it will be interesting indeed Patty. Sam is a cool cucumber under pressure and that's why he is in the side, remember. No point hiding him down the pecking order if he can use his more classic style to keep one end warm while Quince continues to do his thing? Then Bill and Patrick can come in later down the line when the bowlers are a bit more tired, and there are few overs left to start upping the run-rate? The strategy must be one of consolidation now if King is being promoted so urgently."

"Sam King, of Middlesex and now England too, is walking out to the middle for his debut performance. Of course he has made this walk countless times already in his very nascent career, for Middlesex, North London, England Juniors, but a senior cap like this is very different, and we wish him the best of luck. He will need it if he is going to help England to move on to a defendable score here. He will be at the non-striker's end as Shubanka continues from the nursery end."

11:53 **Google Search**: Sam King

Did you mean King Samuel of Bulgaria?

NewsOnline: King scores big in Middlesex Championship promo

30-09-29

Cricknews: Captain King leads Middlesex into div. 1

01-10-29

For more information click here: http://pigeoncricket.com/team/eng/ samking

News Online

Lord's, UK   *30th September 2029*

by Jon Knight

Middlesex celebrated this evening after a win confirmed that Middlesex would be promoted to Division 1 in next year's county championships. This comes after a string of decisive victories for Middlesex away from home, in the last few weeks, culminating in a win here at Lord's against their arch-rivals from South of the River – Surrey.

In the 3 day match, a structure shortened 3 years ago to allow for all the shorter versions of our game to be played in the tight English summer period, Middlesex won the toss and put Surrey into bat. Lord's conditions in September heavily favouring the toss winner, the overcast conditions allowed the ball to swing wildly from the start and Surrey could only manage 133 all out in their first innings, with Alex Quince the pick of the batsmen, carrying his bat for a stoic, but unspectacular, 38 not-out. On the other side Mark Jules, the England future hall-of-famer, did all the damage, as he is accustomed to in these type of conditions, and came home with first innings figures of 13 overs 6 maidens 5 wickets for 28 runs. Middlesex then went to work in the final session of play of the first day, and having lost both openers relatively cheaply the heavens opened up and play was called off for the night at 6:30pm, at which point Middlesex captain Sam King had just come into bat at number 4.

Due to the loss of time on Friday, the second day's play was scheduled to start 1 hour earlier so that as many lost overs could be recovered, with the possibility of play until 7pm. And the conditions could not have been more different; clear skies, sun shining through the few clouds around and Lord's lit up in all its glory. King, who didn't waste any time making the most of the conditions and capitalising on some loose Surrey bowling, put on 165 runs for the third wicket. Marshalling the tail as wickets fell at the other end, he finally holed out in the last hour of the day trying to up the scoring rate, for a massive 233, and a team ended the day with a total of 480 for 8, in 115 overs.

Middlesex then waited until 10am on Sunday morning before confirming that they were declaring on 480-8 and put Surrey back into bat. Having spent the whole of Saturday running all around Lord's, a final day win was almost out of the question for Surrey and it would only be a question of whether they could bat through the 90 overs of the day to draw the match, and deny Middlesex their promotion. However the tiredness got to them and Jules carried on where he had left off on Friday afternoon, although the conditions were not as perfect for swing bowling this time round. He was able to put pressure on the top order, claiming 2 scalps, and was ushered in to clean up the tail when they finally came in, finishing with figures of 4-40. Surrey were only able manage a score of 196 all out, and a combined total of 329 across their two innings. They batted defiantly though in the end were well short of surviving the day, with the last wicket falling at 5:40, with a minimum of 17 overs still to be bowled.

Middlesex then had to wait a nervous hour for confirmation of the draw between Durham and Somerset, which meant that their 5 points (4 for the win and a bonus point for only batting once) was enough to overtake Somerset, who having started a point ahead of them, would only get 2 points for the draw.

As the party was getting underway in the home dressing room at Lord's and spilling out throughout the pavilion I was able to catch up with an inebriated King, the Middlesex captain, and man of the match for his first innings score, and I asked him what it meant to him:

"Jon, hi Jon, Sir Jon, Its incredible! Come join the party. The boys have done a great job all season to get us into a position to win. I'm glad I could do my part when it counted. It's my best score here and the boys just wrote my name onto the England honours board! Don't think it will count though. I'm just so happy. Jules was so good too. Couldn't have done it without him. He can swing that ball around corners. I would have bet money on him getting a 10-for this weekend. We are going to party hard, my friend. Have some champers with us?"

So, Middlesex did what they needed to here and will be playing in the top county division next year. They will have to recover from the hangovers quickly though as the new season will be just around the corner. Their

*first match will be in early March next year, so that there is enough
time for the players to go off to the highly lucrative IPL in April, play
their international summer through June and July and catch up on the
Hundred and the rest of the county season next August and September.
And what for Sam King? I am sure his future is very bright indeed and
he will be knocking on that England door very shortly, if not already
in the picture. You read it here first: that is a future England captain
in the making, and I can talk from experience in saying that getting
drunk at the afterparty is a pre-requisite for that job.*

(Quince upgrades to offensive)

Shubanka to **Quince**, no run, full on the pads and driven back
straight to the bowler.

Shubanka to **Quince**, 4 runs, nice looking shot, driven through a
gap at midwicket against the spin and **Trahar** runs around from the
square leg boundary to cut off the ball but can't get there and it hits
the boundary.

Shubanka to **Quince**, wide, tries to get one spinning around his legs
though doesn't turn nearly enough and in the end is very wide down
the leg side. Smart work from **Singh** to get across and take it cleanly
and avoid any more runs.

Shubanka to **Quince**, no run, off stump line and turning away, left
alone by the batsman.

Shubanka to **Quince**, no run, on line, but it's the googly, or at worst
the one that goes straight on, picked by the batsman and defended
off the back foot.

Shubanka to **Quince**, 2 runs, on the pads and driven off the back
foot past midwicket where **Trahar** has to field it on the boundary in
front of the Grandstand.

Shubanka to **Quince**, 2 runs, over corrected and this is time wide
outside the off stump and the batsmen boldly switches his bat around
and reverse glances fine, past **Pooran** at short third man, who has to
turn and run to catch up with it before it hits the white gates of the

pavilion and they come back for 2.

11:57 England 131-3 after 22 overs. "Good over for Quince there, he seems to have picked up his intent after reaching his 50. Ray can you provide any highlights from that 50 for us?"

"Yes, sure Pat; hi, Andy. Quince is currently 58 not out and so his unique shuffle is clearly working for him. His 50 came off 59 balls, of which 39 were scoring deliveries. He has been hitting the ball to all parts of the ground, without any real danger. Before we even look at it my gut tells me he had quite a symmetric wagon wheel from what I have been watching. Ok so: 18 runs out to midwicket, 17 runs straight down the ground, including that 6 over mid-off I believe, 9 runs through the offside and 6 behind the stumps. So maybe not that symmetric after all, he has preferred straight and on the leg side. I guess him getting across his stumps does help to open that leg side up and the bowlers have obliged him by bowling too straight. There were only 2 boundaries in that 50 which shows the careful type of innings that he is trying to build here, and I guess it's what England need at the moment. England will need him to carry his bat here if he can, and they need him to push on to a ton."

"Thanks Ray, ok so here we are with Sam's first ball for England, he's a leftie so the field has slightly changed around for Pooran, who will continue from the pavilion end. He still has his straight men deep, 3rd man, fine leg, mid-off and mid-on. They have brought in another slip taking out the midwicket man. So, they have an offside heavy 7-2 field with the only protection on the legside at fine leg and deep mid-on. Pooran is going to continue from over the wicket to the leftie, though anything too straight and there is a very inviting gap for him to score in."

Pooran to **King, appeal** for something, short ball on middle and directed at the helmet of the lefthander. He leans across, manages to step back and sway out of the way of it and sort of half falls over. Welcome to international cricket sir. Then there was an appeal by the keeper to the square leg umpire, who is also not very sure what is being appealed for. The keeper is pointing vehemently at the stumps and now celebrating with **Sharma** and his slips **Kumar** and **Bihari. Umpire Du Toit** at square leg is shaking his head but has taken the bait and now refers it to the third umpire. The bail between middle and leg stump is on the ground!

"Umpire to TV director we have an umpire review for bowled can you please check the bowlers footing first? Yes ok seems on the line, fair delivery. Now can I please have the front on view? Ok the ball is pitching, then rising up and to the keeper. That is the ball tracking camera. Do you have anything on the batsmen? Ok here comes the ball, swaying away from it, small stumbling, ok, I don't see anything there, the batsman doesn't touch the ball at all. Do you have a view from behind the stumps? Ok here comes the ball, and the batsman sways back and away from it, and touches the stump? TV director can you please zoom in on the stumps from this angle and rock and roll the delivery for me? Here we go, forward, forward, slowly, there is his leg, and yes it flicks the leg stump as he comes across it. The bail is dislodged. Umpire Randall, can you hear me? I need you to signal the decision as OUT, hit wicket."

11:58

Sam King	hit wicket b. Pooran	0 of 1 ball	FOW: 131-4

CHAPTER 4
ENGLAND 131–4, INDIA YET TO BAT

12:00 "Oh dear, oh dear, oh dear. Andy, listeners, I am absolutely gobsmacked. Sam King on debut has been given out hit wicket, and it seems from the replays that the first ball bouncer from Pooran knocked him backwards and his left leg flicked the bottom of his leg stump just enough to remove the bail. This will not be a debut to remember, a golden duck for the youngster, and a sheepish long walk back to the dressing room."

"Incredible scenes, Patty, I feel so sorry for him. This is going to absolutely hammer his confidence and he may never recover from it. A golden duck on debut, and such a random way to get out, it would be completely unbelievable if I didn't just see it with my own eyes. I don't want to leave but the producer is telling me that I have overstayed my welcome, Bobby Jungan will be joining you for the next session."

"Thanks Andy, and good luck recovering from that one. That takes England to 131 for 4 now and the captain William Jones must come in now to face the music and try and recover this situation? Yes indeed: here he comes down the steps to a standing ovation from the members sitting in the pavilion white benches, and King keeps his eyes locked on the floor as they pass each other. The captain Jones gives him a reassuring tap on the back, before refocusing on the situation and takes long stretching lunges out to the middle, while rotating his midriff and swinging his arms. He is going to have to put in some hard yards here and get England out of this mess of a situation."

"Hi Patty, good afternoon now, what amazing scenes we are watching here. The Indian boys are putting on a show and the Indian in the crowd are going crazy. I'm sure the whole of India is on the edge of their seats, if not on their feet with the excitement of the last 5 minutes. Don't forget Deepak Pooran is on a hat-trick now! He got Barnes at the end of his last over too, although that seems like hours ago!"

"Afternoon Bobby, welcome back to the studio, in all the excitement I forgot to be honest, but yes, for the hat-trick ball Sharma has brought everyone in close. He has completely modified the field. We have 3 slips, a gully, a point, short cover, short mid-on, fine leg and 3rd man. A super-aggressive field for this once-in-a-lifetime opportunity. Jones has made his way to the crease on the nursery end and Sharma has had a quick snipe and smirk at him as he walks past. He will be trying to turn the screw here and get inside the batsman's head. Drum roll for this one Bobby? Here we go.."

Pooran to **Jones**, 2 runs, pressure off immediately, the bowler goes for the pitched-up yorker but gets it wrong and it's a full toss on the pads which can easily be turned away to the wide open legside. **Mopal** fielding temporarily at short mid-on runs down the slope and catches it before it reaches the rope. An easy welcome to the game.

"After the excitement of that last delivery, the field has quickly reverted to something more defensive with men back at their original posts. Sharma has kept the gap open at midwicket, and 2 men in the slip cordon. A full ring around the covers."

Pooran to **Jones**, 1 run, straight and fast, his tail is up, defended down to **Trahar** at deep mid-off.

Pooran to **Quince**, no run, left alone swinging away outside the off stump.

Pooran to **Quince**, 1 run, clipped off the legs down to **Khan** at fine leg.

Pooran to **Jones**, no run, left alone on length, bouncing over off stump with arms shouldered.

12:03   England 135-4 after 23 overs.

Shubanka to **Quince**, 2 runs, reverse sweep playing with the spin of a ball on off stump, hit out past short 3rd man, **Pooran** has to run down to the boundary in front of the Allen Stand where he gets a massive roar from the partisan crowd.

Shubanka to **Quince**, 2 runs, guided very fine of a ball outside leg stump towards the pavilion and **Mopal** fields it from short fine leg.

Shubanka to **Quince**, 1 run, straighter full delivery, driven softly down to **Khan** at deep mid-on for a jogging single.

Shubanka to **Jones**, no run, middle line, defended with a big step forward.

Shubanka to **Jones**, no run, watchful from the batsman, defended down to **Panda** at short leg.

Shubanka to **Jones**, 1 run, full delivery, driven on the leg side down to **Kumar** at deep mid-on.

12:06   England 141-4 after 24 overs.

Pooran to **Jones**, no run, full and outside the off stump, cut at but he was wafting at thin air and no contact made.

Pooran to **Jones**, 6 runs, short delivery at 88mph but wrong line, and the batsman gets into position quickly and helps it on its way of the middle of the bat and over the head of **Khan** at fine leg and into the Edrich Stand. Great timing with very little power, a flick using the pace on the ball and it clears the rope.

Pooran to **Jones**, 2 runs, overcorrects and it's too full this time, clipped off the front foot through the open midwicket area and **Kumar** runs around from deep mid-on to field in front of the Grandstand.

Pooran to **Jones**, no run, better line, outside the off stump and left alone by the batsmen who watches it into the keeper's gloves.

Pooran to **Jones**, 1 run, clipped off the legs down to **Khan** at fine leg.

That's the 150 up for England, and they get a standing ovation from the knowledgeable crowd before it gets shown on the scoreboard.

Pooran to **Quince**, no run, quick and outside off stump, left alone by the batsman.

12:11   England 150-4 after 25 overs. "Well Bobby that is the halfway point of the English innings: how would you rate their performance this morning and the state of the match?"

"Patty it has been a real rollercoaster as Jon and Andy have mentioned already. There have been times of excellence and ordinary from both sides and they have both gotten something out of the morning's action. England's 150 at the halfway stage is already a big score, and they could get 200 in the second half of the innings, which will be above par for this pitch, as they start taking more risks. But on the other hand, 4 down at this stage is also dangerous. Only these two and Sherman are left as recognised top order batsman, and so with a couple more wickets India will be into the tail. Once they are into the tail who knows what can happen, England may not even get to their 50 overs. So very evenly poised at the moment."

"Quince has been batting really well and has upped his intent and aggression in the last few overs?"

"Yes; since he got his 50 he has started playing more elaborate shots, with the sweep and reverse sweep both coming out in that over from Shubanka. He has now had enough time at the crease to get a feel for the conditions and is trying to put the pressure back on India with some positive batting. He needs to take the momentum from them, but it is a difficult task while they are making breakthroughs at the other end. He is a quality player and so needs to make the most of the start he has made here. But he has to be careful and perhaps he has gone too hard too early. There is a lot of time still left in the game. If I was rooting for England I would have asked him to be a bit more conservative until the 35th over? And then open up his arms and try and post something big. 300 is a good score, but all out for 250, trying to go for 350 is not."

11:57 Craig @barmy1992: @PPringles @SirJon @KingSamV is a quality batsman. Got Middx across the line last year with a massive ton. Owns this ground. We need a big one from him.

11:58 Vikas @V4India: @PPringles you need to fire @dizzydora and get a better statsman. Quince only hits the ball off his pads, one dimension to his game! @azerXpress will get him as he walks across his stumps next time.

11:58 Jon Knight @SirJon: *replying to @barmy1992* This is a very different attack to the county Surrey attack. @KingSamV needs to be cautious and take the step up to international level slowly.

11:58 kiks @nikita_aol: @PPringles @dizzydora 2 boundaries in 50 runs is test match batting. Just shows that this is a batting pitch and @KumarRangersIPL will knock them off easily.

11:59 toby @Tobytools: @PPringles @SirJon What are these Indian clowns appealing for??

11:59 Vikas @V4India: @PPringles What's going on? They aren't showing any replays in the stadium! Did he nick it?

12:00 kiks @nikita_aol: @PPringles He kicked it! He Kicked it! Watch his foot!

12:00 toby @Tobytools: @PPringles @SirJon Sit down umpire. The wind blew the bail off. Get your eyes checked. Give @KingSamV the benefit of the doubt.

12:00 kiks @nikita_aol: *replying to @Tobytools* haha @KingSamV he will be able to read those tweets from the locker room now!! Haha!!

12:01 Vikas @V4India: @PPringles He's out! Golden Duck!!! Bye bye! Pooran is on fire here! On a hat-trick! Great to have @Jungan_Official back on commentary!

12:01 Craig @barmy1992: @PPringles @SirJon Oh god! 4 down now! Too much pressure on the debutant! Welcome captain @billythekid. We need a ton from you now!

12:02 Jon Knight @SirJon: *replying to @Tobytools* he flicked the leg stump. Terrible way to get out. Should have ducked out of it rather than sway. He was in two minds.

12:03   **Vikas @V4India:** @PPringles It's party time in the stands here! Barmy army silenced and the Indian army owning lord's today! Chakadeeeeey!

12:04   **toby @Tobytools:** *replying to @SirJon* absolute amateur hour! Who kicks their own stumps? Has this guy not played cricket before? Tell @BCCElive to call me up! I'll last more than a ball against this schoolboy attack.

12:05   **Jon Knight @SirJon:** @PPringles @Jungan_Official Quince has stepped up his game and is bringing out all the shots now. Quality reverse sweeping, got down to the pitch and put it into the gap.

12:07   **Geoff @barmyGeoff:** @PPringles @barmy1992 Boom Boom that's more like it from @billythekid. Pooran is a part timer and deserves to be put into the stands!

12:07   **Craig @barmy1992:** @PPringles ooo dropped in the stands! Protected the beer not the missus - legend! Keep making it rain @billythekid!

12:08   **Bobby @PigeonCricket:** @PPringles @Mikedrop I'm not getting much camera time today?? My agent is doing a terrible job here!

12:09   **Vikas @V4India:** @PPringles great fielding by @KumarRangersIPL in the deep here! Cut off the boundary, full commitment to the country!

12:11   **toby @Tobytools:** @PPringles @Jungan_Official Doubling the score from here should be a minimum respectable target. They should all be fired if they don't get to 300.

12:12   **kiks @nikita_aol:** @PPringles @Jungan_Official This is looking like a 250 all out! The English tail has no staying power. @glassceiling100 won't last much longer than @SamKingV.

12:13   **SC @glassceiling100:** *replying to @nikita_aol* Won't have to test that if these two bat through the rest of the innings! 😎

Shubanka to **Jones**, 1 run, half volley driven down to **Mopal** at deep mid-on.

Shubanka to **Quince**, 4 runs, too short and pulled in front of square over the head of midwicket. One bounce and into the fence in front of the Grandstand.

Shubanka to **Quince**, 1 run, driven off the pads down to **Mopal** for a jogged single.

Shubanka to **Jones**, no run, a well-directed googly picked by the batsman and defended off the back foot to **Panda** at short leg.

Shubanka to **Jones**, 1 run, short and outside, cut away through the covers to **Kapoor,** the sweeper down on the boundary at the bottom of the slope.

Shubanka to **Quince**, 2 runs, short and cut very fine past a dive from **Pooran** at 3rd man, though he is able to recover and collect it before it gets to the boundary.

12:15   England 159-4 after 26 overs.

Pooran to **Jones**, 2 runs, driven off the pads out past a diving midwicket and out towards the cow corner boundary, **Mopal** makes up a lot of ground from deep mid-on to field.

Pooran to **Jones**, no run, great delivery, full though just missing the off stump, swung wildly at by the batsman but no contact. The bowler, keeper and slips all have their hands on their heads in shock at not getting a snick there.

Pooran to **Jones**, 1 run, good line again and solidly defends with some punch down to **Trahar** at deep mid-off.

Pooran to **Quince**, 4 runs, too straight and pulled aggressively off the pads into a gap at midwicket and it is quickly down the slope and into the boundary.

Pooran to **Quince**, 4 runs, this time on the other side, wide outside the off stump and back of a length, quickly cut backward off a diving point who can't get anything on it and it runs out to the rope.

Pooran to **Quince**, no run, angry delivery, short and at the helmet, ducked under, and a sharp jumping one handed save by the wicket keeper.

12:19   England 170-4 after 27 overs. "Bobby, England have really pushed on in the last few overs. Are they in a rush to get somewhere?"

"We were just talking about the 150 up and 2 overs later we are at 170. 2 big overs from England, and it has just been good batting, the bowlers haven't really done anything wrong. Quince is striking the ball right in the middle and the boundaries have started to flow. I think Pooran is getting tired now, losing his concentration. Sunil will need to think about a change at that end and maybe save some of his overs until the end, he was very good at the death in the IPL."

"Well Bobby I think they are making a change though it looks like it's from the other end, Varun Mopal is coming on to bowl from the nursery end. I think they are scared of what Quince may do to the spinners? He is seeing the ball as if it's a football and there isn't much spin of variation from them. So it will be Mopal to replace Shubanka from the Nursery end."

Mopal to **Jones**, no run, wayward outside the off stump and left alone by the batsman.

Mopal to **Jones**, no run, straighter line, and defended off a good length on the back foot back to the bowler who fields it with his foot.

Mopal to **Jones**, 6 runs, short and pulled away high of the front foot, it is up in the air for a very long time and finally comes down into the second row of the lower Grandstand. You can't bowl there with no protection on that square leg boundary. All the men outside the 30 yards circle are straight, so it's a risk-free shot to try and hit uppish and square. This time he makes full middle contact and it sails over the ropes.

Mopal to **Jones**, 1 run, quickly off strike with a safe shot down to **Pooran** at deep mid-on.

Mopal to **Quince**, 4 runs, driven on the half volley through a gap between cover and point and it races quickly down the slope and bounces off the advertising hoardings and into the first row of the stands.

Mopal to **Quince**, no run, same angle, same direction, though 20 mph slower and not picked by the batsman as he goes for the big drive and it misses everything.

12:24   England 181-4 after 28 overs. "Bobby, to be honest they didn't need to protect the spinners that much, that was a woeful over. Mopal was all over the place. Is it really that much harder for them bowling up from that side? We are going to get a change at the pavilion end too. Captain Sharma agreed with you that Pooran looks tired, and we are going to get Azer Khan back from this, his preferred end. He is going for quite an aggressive field though, 2 slips and the only 2 men outside the circle at 3rd man and fine leg. It's as if he was still bowling in the power play? I think they are setting him up to try and take some wickets, and they don't mind if he is a little expensive. Lets see what happens."

Khan to **Jones**, 2 runs, clipped off his legs past midwicket and down the hill, **Sharma** has to chase it back and dives to pull it in before it reaches the rope. **Mopal** helps him out and gets the ball back to the keeper.

Khan to **Jones**, 2 runs, short ball and pulled, though high on the bat and it balloons out into the vacant square leg area where **Umpire Randall** has to duck out of the way. **Sharma** has to chase it out from midwicket again and they get back for 2.

Khan to **Jones**, no run, straighter line and length and defended out to **Panda** at point off the back foot.

Khan to **Jones**, no run, fiery delivery, at 87mph, though targeted outside the off stump and left alone by the batsman.

Khan to **Jones**, 2 runs, full delivery driven hard through the covers and a dive from **Kapoor**, stops the boundary but the ball continues to trickle down there. They get back for the second because of the misfield, but really it saved a boundary.

Khan to **Jones**, no run, short and at the body, defended down to **Sharma** at midwicket.

12:28   England 187-4 after 29 overs.

Mopal to **Quince**, 2 runs, short and outside off stump cut away backward of point towards the Tavern Stand, **Shubanka** makes up a lot of ground from wide 3rd man to cut off the boundary and they get back for the second on the throw to the bowler's end.

Mopal to **Quince, bowled**, short and wide delivery outside off stump, cut at by the batsman who can only chop it down off the bottom edge and it bounces up to take the top of leg stump.

12:30

| Alex Quince | b. Mopal | 85 off 81 balls | FOW: 189-5 |

"That brings an end to the Quince show, a fantastic knock by the England opener who departs for an enviable 85 runs off 81 balls. He tried to cut the wide delivery from Mopal into the same gap as he had the ball before though could only get a bottom edge and unluckily it hits his leg stump. Terrible fortune, but could this breakthrough change the game for India, Bobby?"

"You know the old saying Patty, it is sometimes better to be lucky than good and that is what Mopal will be thinking right now. His first over back got taken for a few runs, and his second didn't start much better, wide and not that quick. But he is celebrating now. I think he would have wanted to get Barnes because of their time together in the IPL, though he will be happy enough with this one, especially if it gets India some of the momentum back."

"So Quince takes the long walk back to the pavilion and gets a well-deserved standing ovation from the crowd. He would have liked to get to that 100 and get on the honours board but it is not to be today, as he falls 15 runs short. The Indian and English crowd know they have been well entertained and are giving him a congratulatory salute as he holds up his bat to the different parts of the stadium. It will be Patrick Sherman next in, the England all-rounder, who completed his residency in the UK just last year after transferring from the Caribbean 4 years ago. He is met by the captain halfway back to the pavilion and they are in deep discussion. Sherman is the last recognised batsman that England has and so these two will need to put in a stint here, there are still a lot of overs left in this match."

"To be honest Patty, I don't know much about Sherman, so I am going to give my seat back to Jon, who has been watching him more closely over the last couple of months. I will join you again later this afternoon for the India innings."

"Patty, hello again and good afternoon. Sherman is certainly coming in at a precarious time for England here and will have to do something for his adopted nation and quickly. We know he can hit to all parts but I think this is untested water, 20 overs or so still to go , plenty of time to get your eye in and build an innings. He doesn't need to go big hitting from the first ball, but I fear that's the only style he has. Back in the West Indies they are now only taught to play one-way, big hitting, big entertainment, but I think it's too early for that. Bill will have to try and keep his head screwed on and not give away his wicket, at least for another 10 overs over so."

"Jon, I have never seen Sherman try to defend. That's why he is so destructive as a batsman, if he gets going. He is going to try to tee it off, and normally that works pretty well for him. Down under over the winter he was able to turn games at this stage of the innings, and demoralise the Aussies, which is easier said than done. Personally, I am looking forward to his battle with Azer. Azer was his captain at Jaipur in the IPL and they would have spent a lot of time together. He would have faced off a lot in the nets and also discussed plans with him as a bowling unit. Of course the situation and conditions are very different here, and Azer hasn't had any success yet, but we and Sherman know he is world class and a game- changer."

(*Sherman upgrades to offensive*)

"**Mopal** to **Sherman**, wide, targeted at the body but down the legside and is left alone by the batsman for an easy wide call by **Umpire Randall.**

Mopal to **Sherman**, no run, targeted at the body again, but straighter and defended out to **Kumar** at midwicket.

Mopal to **Sherman**, 1 run, on the legs and clipped down to the **Khan** at fine leg, a bit of the inside edge of his bat.

Mopal to **Jones**, 2 runs, offside and short, cut past **Panda** at point and out to **Shubanka** at 3rd man. They are quick between the wickets and take on the throw for a second run.

Mopal to **Jones**, no run, short and straight defended on tip-toes straight back to the bowler.

12:33   England 193-5 after 30 overs.

Khan to **Sherman**, 1 run, straight yorker dug out and the ball scuttles out to a gap at square leg, where **Sharma** has to run around to field.

Khan to **Jones**, 6 runs, short and wide and gets the full treatment of the middle of the bat, hit high over the point fielder into the advertising hoardings over the boundary rope. Easy pickings. That brings up the 200 runs for England. The batsmen meet in the middle for a celebratory handshake and they get a full round of applause from the crowd.

Khan to **Jones**, no run, full and cutting into the right hander, defended solidly on the front foot.

Khan to **Jones**, 1 bye, short and ducked under, the keeper has to jump and can only get a part of the glove to it; the ball trickles down to **Pooran** at fine leg.

Khan to **Sherman**, no run, straight and fast, defended out to **Sharma** at midwicket.

Khan to **Sherman**, no run, outside the line and left alone, the batsman watches it through to the keeper.

12:38   England 201-5 after 31 overs. "Jon, Bill brings up the 200 for England in style with a big shot over point, how is their situation looking?"

"Patty it was a big shot, but really was the only loose delivery in that Khan over. Apart from that one ball he was really on top of the batsmen, especially the new guy. The ball is moving around off the seam and that yorker first ball to Sherman was fantastic, he is lucky he got something on it. Overall 200 at the 31st over is a solid position though they are 5 down already. Jules is in next and no one classes him as a batsman, so they need to be careful of their wickets."

"Ray, jump in here, you have some stats for us on Quince's innings?"

"Yes, Pat, Jon, good afternoon: what an innings it was. 85 at over a run a ball. As we mentioned with his 50 the runs were mainly coming in singles and twos, and mainly towards midwicket. After he got to his 50 he started to open up his arms and the creativity and the boundaries starting flowing. The next 35 runs came in only 14 balls including 5 fours. His main innings highlight came early on in his innings though when he hit Khan back over his head for 6 down the ground. That should make the game highlight reel, otherwise a very steady innings. Overall 37% of Quince's runs came through midwicket, and over half on the legside. The Indians didn't have an answer for his trigger shuffle move, bowling too much on middle and towards leg. 43% of all the deliveries he faced were on middle or down the legside, which at this level is not good enough, and those were easy pickings for him as he walked across the stumps. The Indian bowling unit needs to have a better plan as they meet him again in the rest of this series."

"Thanks Ray, that's really interesting, you would have thought Chris Hollier would have instilled in all his bowlers a strict off stump or 4th

stump line, but maybe they couldn't execute that in these conditions. Anyway, let's get back out to the two that are out there at the moment, Mopal continuing from the Nursery end."

Mopal to **Jones**, 1 run, clipped off the legs down to **Khan** at fine leg.

Mopal to **Sherman**, no run, back of a length and outside off stump line left alone by the batsman.

Mopal to **Sherman**, 2 runs, full and straight, goes for the straight drive and gets an inside edge and the ball runs out into the gap at square leg, **Kumar** runs around from midwicket to field it, but **Sherman** is very quick and calls **Jones** back for the second. There is a shy at the single stump though it misses and is backed up by **Panda.**

Mopal to **Sherman**, no run, back of a length and rising, a wild swing by the batsman out towards cow corner, though he misses it completely and it hits him in the stomach.

Mopal to **Sherman**, **bowled**, good length delivery, he attempts a big drive at the ball, but it cuts in off the seam a bit and goes past the bat, through the gate, and smashes into the off stump, knocking it to 45 degrees. The bowler gets his reward and celebrates by being surrounded by his teammates.

12:42

Patrick Sherman   b. Mopal   4 of 10 balls   FOW: 204-6

"That brings an end to Sherman's short stay at the crease and he didn't really trouble the scorers too much. His swashbuckling attitude never looked comfortable with lots of swings and misses. This bowling change now looks very inspired by Sharma, and his first change bowler, Mopal, has come through for him. We are now through the recognised batsmen for England and into the tail, with England fast bowler Mark Jules coming to the crease next. Captain Jones is going to have to marshal the tail well here if England are going to last the remaining 19 overs."

Mopal to **Jules**, 1 run, thick edge of a good ball down past the slips to **Shubanka** at 3rd man.

12:44   England 205-6 after 32 overs.

Khan to **Jules**, 2 runs, full ball driven back past the bowler, great shot just past the non-striker's stumps, towards the pavilion, through the flock of pigeons who go flying off into the air. **Trahar** and **Mopal** both chase after it and jointly collect it in front of the members and get it back to the bowler.

Khan to **Jules**, no run, straight and fast, defended on the back foot. A couple of pigeons have now landed down on the playing pitch and are scared away by **Jules** who aims a big kick at them. The don't seem to take much notice and he has to chase them across two wickets before they are clear of the pitch. *Follow all our pigeon action live across social media @PigeonCricket.*

Khan to **Jules**, 2 runs, full and driven again past the bowler and straight fielders. They come back for 2 as **Trahar** fields.

Khan to **Jules**, no run, full and off stump, swung at but completely missed and through the keeper.

Khan to **Jules**, no run, back of length and defended on the back foot.

Khan to **Jules**, 1 run, edged and a chance at second slip goes down. **Jones** calls through for a quick single even though it is the end of the over.

12:48   England 210-6 after 33 overs.

Mopal to **Jules**, 1 run, clipped of the pads and sent down to **Khan** at fine leg.

Mopal to **Jones**, no run, strong drive on the front foot but fielded well by a diving **Panda** at point to stop the single.

Mopal to **Jones**, 4 runs, expertly cut between point and cover this time and the ball runs to the boundary in front of the Grandstand.

Mopal to **Jones**, 4 runs, too straight and too full, driven back past the bowler and in between the 2 deep straight fielders to the boundary in front of the Media Centre.

Mopal to **Jones**, no run, good reply from **Mopal**, back of a length and can only be defended back to the bowler off the front foot.

Mopal to **Jones**, 2 runs, stepped across the stumps and clipped off the pad into the square leg gap. **Khan** and **Kumar** from fine leg and midwicket work in tandem to stop the boundary and limit the damage to 2. That brings up William Jones' 50 and he raises his bat to the applauding crowd without taking off his helmet. It is a muted celebration as there is still much work to do, and he gets a tap on the back from his batting partner.

12:52   England 221-6 after 34 overs. "Jon, that has been an excellent knock from the captain?"

"Yes indeed Patty, just what England needed in this innings. Some stability while keeping the scoring rate ticking over. He has played some excellent shots all around the ground without being aggressive and without taking any risks. It is this type of batting that has got him to be one of the best one-day batsmen in the world, and his ability to absorb pressure and throw it back at his opponents is why he is a great captain too."

"The 12th men are running onto the field again and we are going to take our second drinks break of the innings. The weather so far has stayed very fair as expected, though most of the Indians have not taken off their jumpers yet. The England batsmen are batting in their t-shirts, so it can't be too cold out there in the midday sunshine. Ray can you tell us about that 50?"

"Yes Patty, it was a very quick 50 indeed, coming off only 39 balls, including two 4s and three 6s. 13 runs coming through the covers, 9 runs down the ground straight and 18 runs though midwicket: it is a very well spread wagon wheel. The highlights were the sixes, which have been over fine leg, off Pooran I believe, one over midwicket and then that glorious upper cut off Khan. He has upped his scoring rate in the last few overs, with only 18 runs coming off his first 20 balls and 32 off the last 19."

"Thanks Ray, India are now going to make a change from the pavilion end now and Nikil Panda, the allrounder off spinner, is coming back on. They are saving the last 2 Khan overs for the real death? They have quite a tight aggressive field for Jules, a slip and both silly point and short leg. Deep protection at square leg and a sweeper on the offside. 2 men also straight on the boundary, with 3rd man and fine leg inside the circle. He hasn't bowled from this end yet as it has been reserved for the quicks though he will be happy that the short boundary is not on the leg side anymore. Taking his time to get the field in the right areas with lots of arm waving, whilst spinning the old ball between his fingers. Will it turn this time?"

Panda to **Jules, bowled**, straight through the gate of the tailender as he swings wildly at one that spins from off to middle a little and it clatters into the bail between off and middle stump.

12:55

Mark Jules   b. Panda   7 off 8 balls   FOW: 221-7

"Does the damage with his first ball! Seemed like lots of turn from up here, Jon? The slope was probably helping him a little bit. But a terrible shot from Jules? Trying to smash it out of the park without facing this bowler before? He is furious with himself and captain Jones is furious with him too. He has to walk past him back to the pavilion and he gets a cold dark stare from the captain, a criminal attempt at a shot."

"It was his temperament that undid him there Patty, but he isn't a batsman so we can't berate him too much. He was trying to play it as he saw it and was probably expecting a loosener from Panda first up which he could have had a go at. If he had connected would have probably reached that Grandstand boundary over the covers, and would have set the terms of the contest between them, but that's all history now."

"England are collapsing? They were in a very strong position at 122 for 2 back in the 20th over at 221-7 it is a very different story. They will not be able to accelerate at the back end of the innings for fear of not getting to the end?"

"Bobby Jungan, when he was on earlier, called it completely correctly, they could get all out for 250 trying to chase 350, when 300 would probably be respectable. With the batting to come I think 300 is a very long way off now and if Bill can get them another 50 or so runs in the next 15 overs then they will take 280 given where they are right now. The Indians will try and keep Bill off strike and try to plough through Sonia, Hunter and Mo. He is really going to have to use his head to get to the end, as the rest of them can't be expected to bat against a top bowling attack like India's. Sonia is in next, a crowd favourite on both side, so she will get support from them, but Sharma knows her game, and knows where she is weak, so will have a plan."

"Indeed Andy, Sonia Chancellor has got her pads on and strides out to the middle having been promoted up the order before the start of play to number 8, ahead of Hunter French. She has lots of experience of this Indian bowling attack having faced them all recently out at the IPL. Although she didn't really do that much batting until a few weeks ago at the Mumbai vs Mohali match where she was able to guide Mumbai to a 3 wicket win with some sensible batting. She couldn't help Mumbai qualify for the playoffs though and she was back in the UK preparing for this tournament just a week later."

"Yes I watched that one on YouTube actually and she came up against Nikil Panda there. As usual he opened the bowling for Mohali and so she didn't face him directly, but would know his style very well and will know what to expect. I think she will be more dangerous against Shubanka though. They are both leggies, and I know that she has been watching and learning from his tricks a lot to help her own bowling. That should make it easier for her to pick his variations and maybe score some runs. Shubanka has 5 overs left still so if she can see off the quicks then she may get a chance."

"Yes that's right Jon, Shubanka has 5 overs left, Panda has another 4 after this one. Mopal only has 1, Azer 2 and Pooran 3. So Panda to continue to Chancellor."

Panda to **Chancellor**, 1 run, off the mark straight away, short delivery pulled away to square leg and **Trahar** fields on the boundary.

Panda to **Jones**, 2 runs, premeditated reverse sweep on a back of a length ball clipped down past **Bihari** at slip who has to chase it down to the boundary to collect.

Panda to **Jones**, no run, defended back to the bowler.

Panda to **Jones**, 1 run, the field comes in to prevent the single though a full delivery is squeezed out towards midwicket and **Mopal** cannot get around quickly enough before the single is taken.

Panda to **Chancellor**, 1 run, on the off stump and neatly driven towards **Kapoor** on the cover boundary. The batswomen calls for a run loudly, catching the non-striker a bit off guard, who was expecting to hold his ground and then keep the strike for the next over.

12:40   **toby @Tobytools:** no @PPringles, what @dizzydora said it not that interesting. Who cares how many runs Quince scored off his pads. He couldn't get 100. He let the side down when they needed him. Period.

12:42   **Vikas @V4India:** @PPringles @SirJon Patrick Sherman was useless in the IPL. He couldn't get Jaipur to qualify for the playoffs after all that money they spent on him. Useless. Chakde Mumbai!

12:43   **kiks @nikita_aol:** *replying to @V4India* Mumbai didn't qualify for the playoffs either, mate!

12:43   **Vikas @V4India:** *replying to @nikita_aol* Yeah but Mumbai didn't spend all that money at the auction! Doesn't matter anyway - Sherman is gone! Thanks for playing, see you next time!

12:44   **toby @Tobytools:** *replying to @nikita_aol* Are you still using AOL? Do they not have proper internet in India yet?

12:45 **Craig @barmy1992:** @PPringles @SirJon what a shot by @jules_england, straight back through the pigeons

12:45 **Bobby @PigeonCricket:** @PPringles @Mikedrop Oi!! @jules_england can you not let me have my lunch in peace?? So rude!

12:46 **Bobby @PigeonCricket:** @PPringles Come here @jules_england and say it to my face! I've got my buddies! Wait.. I'm on TV again!

12:47 **Vikas @V4India:** @PPringles Look at this guy! Dancing around with @PigeonCricket. How are England going to rely on this guy for anything. Even the pigeons aren't scared of him.

12:52 **Geoff @barmyGeoff:** @PPringles @barmy1992 @billythekid lighting up lord's now! Boom Boom, sending Mopal to all parts. Great 50 sir, well batted.

12:53 **Craig @barmy1992:** *replying to @barmyGeoff* no worries mate @billythekid will see us to the end! In our captain we trust!

12:55 **Vikas @V4India:** *replying to @V4India* See what I mean! @jules_england can't bat! Get back in the clubhouse! @greatwhitepanda making it happen!

12:55 **kiks @nikita_aol:** *replying to @V4India* did you just reply to your own tweet?

12:55 **kiks @nikita_aol:** *replying to @glassceiling100* welcome to the game Sonia. I guess you can reply to this in 5 mins when you are back in the locker room.

12:56 **Vikas @V4India:** *replying to @nikita_aol* I'm just saying @greatwhitepanda is someone Mumbai should have bought, not @glassceiling100! He's a gamechanger. Gets it done with the bat and ball.

12:56 **kiks @nikita_aol:** *replying to @V4India* @glassceiling100 maybe useless, but cheap at $2m or whatever Mumbai paid. They must have sold a Chancellor shirt to every girl in India! Doubt anyone buys her England shirt.

12:57 **Vikas @V4India:** @SirJon are you saying that @glassceiling100 is better than Shubanka? How biased are you?

12:58 **toby @Tobytools:** *replying to @V4India* nah @SirJon was saying that they were equally useless! How did they let this woman in the team? To make the lunches?

12:59 **Geoff @barmyGeoff:** @PPringles @barmy1992 @billythekid is going to have to protect @glassceiling100 if England have a chance. Can they get to 300?

12:59 **Vikas @V4India:** *replying to @barmyGeoff* fat chance. All out for 250, you heard it here first!

12:59 **kiks @nikita_aol:** *replying to @Tobytools* so you are a sexist and a racist?

13:00 **toby @Tobytools:** *replying to @nikita_aol* How am I a racist? It's good that India has internet, even if it is AOL. But sure @glassceiling100 can make me breakfast anytime if you know what I mean!

13:00 **kiks @nikita_aol:** *replying to @Tobytools* You are a pig! Get lost.

CHAPTER 5
ENGLAND 229-7, INDIA YET TO BAT

13:00 "Welcome back to the commentary box Andy, Jon will be taking a break, what does Bill have to do now to save this innings? I'm sure he has to protect Sonia as much as he can?"

"Without a doubt. It has been an exciting watch so far from the cheap seats, and it's really on a knife edge. The boys, and girl, will now need to be extra conservative to make sure England are still batting when we get to 50 overs. Personally, I think it will be tough. The Indians are full of energy in the field and will be expecting to rip through this tail as quickly as possible. They will be looking to restrict England to something less than 280, and then be expecting to chase it down quite easily. All the pressure is certainly on Jones now. He will have to knock it around gently, retain as much of the strike as possible, and hope he can see them through until over 45 at least. Then they will have a chance to open up their arms in the last 5 and try and sneak an extra 40 runs. England only get to 300 if he is still there at the end, I think."

"India will have an aggressive strategy now. First up it's Mopal to finish his last one for the day, and for some reason Sonia called Bill through for a single at the end there and will be facing. Not sure if she got the memo, but clearly she is out there to make a statement that she can bat."

Mopal to **Chancellor**, 2 runs, full delivery, driven with a straight bat back past the bowler. The straight fielders are up to the tailender and **Trahar** catches up to it in front of the Media Centre.

Mopal to **Chancellor**, no run, outside the off stump and left alone.

Mopal to **Chancellor**, 1 run, edge and chance goes begging at slip as the ball runs down to **Shubanka** at 3rd man. Not sure if it carried but **Bihari** wasn't able to get a hand on it and **Mopal** is shaking his head in disappointment.

Mopal to **Jones**, no run, outswinging delivery left alone by the batsman outside the off stump.

Mopal to **Jones**, wide, tries to correct the line and overcorrects and it trundles down the leg side. Smart take by **Singh** diving to his left.

Mopal to **Jones**, no run, short and left alone outside the off stump. The field is up to prevent the single.

Mopal to **Jones**, no run, full delivery outside off stump which is swung at though with no contact and it goes through to the keeper.

13:04   England 230-7 after 37 overs. "Andy, it seems like Bill is going to let Sonia bat a bit. He didn't really look like forcing a single at the end of that last over. I guess he has some confidence in her?"

"He was saying at the top of the innings that he had been impressed with the improvement in her batting, though I agree, the fewer balls she faces the better for England. Anyway, that was the end of Mopal's second spell and in the end he finishes with figures of 10 overs, no maidens, 2 wickets for 65 runs. A bit on the expensive side though he got 2 crucial wickets in that second spell. Firstly, finally removing Alex Quince who looked set for a century, and then in quick succession, Sherman, who didn't really trouble the scorers too much. Captain Sharma will be quite happy with Mopal's return for the day and now will put him out to pasture on one of the boundaries as a well done. Panda is going to continue."

Panda to **Chancellor**, no run, defended stoutly on middle stump.

Panda to **Chancellor**, 1 run, clipped off middle out to **Trahar** at deep square leg.

Panda to **Jones**, no run, outside the off stump and full, left alone by the batsman.

Panda to **Jones**, 1 run, full on off stump again, this time driven up the hill, out to the sweeper **Kapoor**, on the cover boundary in front of the Grandstand.

Panda to **Chancellor**, 1 run, full again but on leg stump and driven straight down the ground to **Mopal** at deep mid-on.

Panda to **Jones**, 2 runs, reverse sweep off a back of the length ball just past **Bihari** at slip who has to chase it down towards the Media centre and catches up to it just in front of the boundary.

13:07   England 235-7 after 38 overs. "India are going to bring spin on from both ends here to give the quicks some rest. Shubanka still has 5 overs left so he will have to bowl all the way through to the end. He has been expensive so far, going for 37 in those 5 overs, though England are in a defensive mood now. Very different circumstances to his first spell and the older ball now will also help. They are sticking with a defensive field: no men under the helmet, 2 men deep straight and 2 men on either side sweeping. Let's see if he can make an impact."

Shubanka to **Chancellor**, no run, middle line, staying straight, defended.

Shubanka to **Chancellor**, no run, off stump line and spinning away, left alone. Some decent turn there, using a bit of the slope.

Shubanka to **Chancellor**, no run, oh good ball, turning away and just missing the bat from a tentative forward defensive shot. Bowler, keeper and slip all have their hands on their heads, they don't know how it didn't get an edge.

Shubanka to **Chancellor**, no run, driven off the back foot, but smartly stopped by **Sharma**, diving at short extra cover to stop any chance of a single.

Shubanka to **Chancellor**, 1 run, finally she manages to get him away down to **Khan** at deep mid-off.

Shubanka to **Jones**, 2 runs, swept off the front foot to a back of a length ball, against the spin, down past short fine leg and the sweeper **Trahar** has to run around and cut off the boundary.

13:10   England 238-7 after 39 overs. "Patty, that was a very well-controlled over from Shubanka and he had Sonia very contained. Lovely flight on the ball and he is getting some turn. To be honest Sonia should know exactly how to pick him. She has been studying his action and effectiveness for her own leg spin and so should be able to pick up on all his hand positions when facing. She also came up against him in the IPL, though Bangalore thrashed her Mumbai twice so not sure if she had enough time to learn anything from him there. Jones needs to open up his shoulders now, he can't afford to have another 3 run over at this stage, otherwise they won't have anything defendable. 11 overs left they need to be thinking at least 6 an over, to get to 300."

Panda to **Chancellor**, 2 runs, nice shot off a full delivery, driven down the ground past **Sharma** at mid-off and fielded by **Mopal**, running around from deep mid-on and helping out his captain.

Panda to **Chancellor**, no run, outside of the off stump and left alone. The batswoman is shocked that it hasn't been called a wide by **Umpire du Toit**.

Panda to **Chancellor**, 1 run, short ball pulled away to the leg side and fielded by **Trahar** coming in off the boundary.

Panda to **Jones**, 1 run, short again and pulled by the captain this time out to **Trahar** at deep square leg. He is getting a lot of activity down the slope there and protecting that boundary well.

Panda to **Chancellor**, no run, good line and length delivery and defended. Nothing she could do with that ball.

Panda to **Chancellor**, no run, this time she gets it away out into the covers and it is fielded by **Kapoor**, though the non-striker denies the call for a run and stays where he is to keep the strike.

13:13 England 242-7 after 40 overs. "Another very poor over from England at this stage of the match. 10 overs – they need at least 60 runs to make this competitive. Another problem they have – we are now into the third power play of the match, India are now allowed up to 5 fielders outside the 30 yard ring. For Shubanka they are sticking with only 4 outside the ring at the moment, evidence from that first over suggest that he is bowling tightly enough to manage the situation."

(Jones and Chancellor both upgrade to offensive)

Shubanka to **Jones**, 2 runs, clipped off the pads, against the spin, past midwicket and in between deep square leg and deep mid-on, and **Trahar** gets there just on the boundary line to collect.

Shubanka to **Jones**, 2 runs, back of a length and neatly cut past point and down the hill, though **Kapoor** runs around to sweep.

Shubanka to **Jones**, 4 runs, smashed over the head of midwicket into the gap and with one bounce it is over the boundary. Hitting against the spin though getting the middle of the bat on it.

Shubanka to **Jones**, no run, off the pads and clipped to **Panda** at midwicket.

Shubanka to **Jones**, **caught**, full straight delivery and driven very high and straight back over the bowler's head going for the maximum, though it is too high and it's a very long way to the Media Centre boundary. **Khan** is able to set himself and take a straightforward catch just inside the rope.

13:16

William Jones	c. Khan	68 off 57 balls	FOW: 250-8
	b. Shubanka		

"The captain has holed out to deep mid-on! What a time for Shubanka to take his first wicket and this now leaves England in a very perilous position."

"Indeed Patty; he had just started to turn up the scoring rate with 8 off the first 3 balls of that over but then just couldn't get it over the rope. The ball was definitely there to be hit, full and not moving that much, he will be utterly disappointed that he couldn't clear Khan. As he walks back to the pavilion he is practising that big shot, maybe he hit it a bit high on the bat?"

"It skyrocketed straight off the bat, and lost a lot of its power going up rather than long. In the end it was quite a straightforward wicket and the Indians know they have made a real breakthrough there. Well Andy, the tail really needs to come to England's rescue here. It's Hunter French to the wicket now. Without wishing to do Mo Khan any injustice I would say that Hunter is the last one who can hold a bat, and he will be going out there with something to prove. He has been demoted down behind Sonia today and he will want to show his captain and coach that he can be trusted with batting duties."

"Last year I made the call to keep Hunter ahead of Sonia, even though she was improving, and he did deliver when given the chance. However she proved herself during the recent IPL and just got the nod ahead today. Anyway she is still there and they will now have to work together to progress England to something defendable. Now that Jones is back in the hut, 280 will be a good score. But the way the Indians are jumping around, they will be expecting this innings to be all over in the next few overs. Ray what can you tell us about the captain's innings?"

"Andy, this is not a great time to lose our captain, but he steadied the ship quite nicely since they were in a perilous position at 131-4. He has gotten them up to 250 now, in pretty quick time. His innings in particular: 68 runs off 57 balls, 3 sixes, all of which will be on the highlights reel, and 3 fours. This ground is long and so most of his runs actually came in twos! His wagon wheel is quite spread out, as we would expect from Bill, he is talented enough to score in all parts of the ground and doesn't really have a favoured side. This time, 11 runs came straight, 16 runs behind square, 16 into the covers and 25 through midwicket. He gave punishment to all the bowlers, but got the most out of Mopal, taking 20 off him including a six and two fours. All in all a good performance, though in the circumstances, he will be angry with himself that he couldn't last out until the end. Looking forward, as Patty has said, Mo doesn't have a good record here, or anywhere really, so French and Chancellor will have to bat sensibly and solidly if they want to get to the end. But getting to the end at 3 or 4 runs an over will only get them to 290, and so that might not be the best strategy. If they see something hittable, they need to go after it. That just my two cents."

"Thanks Ray, Sonia and Bill, crossed while the ball was up in the air so she will face Shubanka's last ball of the over."

Shubanka to **Chancellor**, wide, its down the legside and wide. She tried to sweep it though made no contact and **Umpire Randall** opens his arms wide.

Shubanka to **Chancellor**, 4 runs, full toss, pulled wide of midwicket strongly and into the Grandstand fence. She gets a solid fist bump from her batting partner as they meet at the end of the over.

13:19   England 255-8 after 41 overs. "Panda has 2 overs left, and he is going for a very aggressive field. Men around the bat and only protection on the boundary on the leg side. He and Sharma know they are into the real tail now and will be wanting to put maximum pressure on them."

(French upgrades to offensive)

Panda to **French**, no run, defended on the off stump back to the bowler.

Panda to **French**, 2 runs, full delivery driven back past the bowler down towards the pavilion. The boundary is very long down there and **Mopal** can chase it in before it gets there.

Panda to **French, bowled**, spinning it goes straight through the gate as the batsman attempts a wild drive and hits the stumps halfway up middle.

13:21

| Hunter French | b. Panda | 2 off 3 balls | FOW: 257-9 |

"Patty, he went for a big drive there and this innings is coming to an end now very quickly! He didn't need to go so aggressive so quickly, especially against a spinner who has already had so much success on this pitch. Panda gets his fourth wicket for the day and will be gunning for that five-for now. The final man to the crease is our Mohammed Khan, who has a whopping 8 overs to survive just to get to the end of the innings. It's going to be a very tall task unless Sonia can keep all of the strike and protect him very well."

"Unfortunately that is Hunter's style. He had something to prove and would have been hoping to light up the crowd with some big shots. It wasn't the right time for it and his teammates won't be thanking him at all, though unlike some of the top order batsmen he will have a chance to redeem himself with the ball. Now that we are getting to the end of the innings let me tell you all what we have planned for the lunch break. Firstly we will be getting Mike to speak to Captain Jones and Sharma to see how they assess the first innings performance from both of their teams. After that I have the pleasure of inviting His Royal Highness the Duke of Exeter, President of the Board of Control for Cricket in England, to the commentary box to get some of his thoughts on the match situation, his plans for English cricket over the coming years and if I can I will ask him how he and his family have been handling the constitutional crises that we have been facing in the last few years. It has certainly been a very interesting time for the British Royal Family and hopefully he can share some insights on how his nephew King William is getting on in his new role. But before all of that intrigue, Panda still has one more to get for his five-for and England still have another 8 overs to last, if they can. Panda will come around the wicket to Mohammed Khan as the left hander asks for a middle and leg stump guard. There are fielders all around the bat as they try to finish this off."

13:04   **Vikas @V4India:** @PPringles lovely spell there from Mopal! He is the work horse of this Indian team. No heroics just keeps his head down and does his business.

13:06   **toby @Tobytools:** *replying to @V4India* Work horse? More like work donkey. Average bowler at the bottom of an average attack. Quince got out trying to smash him out of the park, and that exactly what he deserved.

13:10   **toby @Tobytools:** @PPringles @SirJon Are England playing a test match here? 3 an over is not going to win this.

13:11   **Vikas @V4India:** *replying to @Tobytools* Lord's is a test venue after all! Maybe they are trying to get on the test honours boards. Haha.

13:11   **Geoff @barmyGeoff:** @PPringles @barmy1992 At some point @billythekid has to go for it and start smashing these spinners into the stands no?

13:12   **Craig @barmy1992:** *replying to @barmyGeoff* The hare loses in the end mate! Slow and steady. Get to the 50 overs.

13:17   **Vikas @V4India:** *replying to @barmyGeoff* And he's out of here!! Straight down Azer's throat. England are finished here now. All out in the next 10 mins? @frenchcricket, @glassceiling100 and @MoKduck aren't going to hang around very long.

13:18   **toby @Tobytools:** @PPringles @SirJon Are you serious!!? He puts it right in the slot and @billythekid holes out? Screw this England team.

13:19   **toby @Tobytools:** @PPringles oh and @dizzydora can shove it too! No one cares about your two cents.

13:20   **kiks @nikita_aol:** *replying to @Tobytools* @SirJon can someone just ban this guy from posting? Spews complete rubbish all the time. @dizzydora – doing a good job sir, bring on the stats!

13:21   **Geoff @barmyGeoff:** @PPringles @barmy1992 Boom! That's more like it @glassceiling100! Lets finish this innings off in style. Get us to 300!

13:22   **Vikas @V4India:** *replying to @V4India* I called it!! The Indians are cleaning up the tail now! Chakaaaaadey!!!

13:22   **Craig @barmy1992:** *replying to @barmyGeoff* OMG, @frenchcricket has played all around that one! Wasn't even that good a ball. It's simple: bat on ball, ball into stands.

13:23   **Geoff @barmyGeoff:** *replying to @barmy1992* Too true my friend, too true! @abirdman is right – he just comes out swinging with no thought of the situation. Terrible shot at a terrible time. Going from bad to worse.

13:23   **kiks @nikita_aol:** *replying to @V4India* Time for @GreatWhitePanda to clean up @MoKDuck and claim his 5-for here. He has 9 balls left to make it happen. @CaptianSharma don't you dare take him off!

Panda to **Khan**, 2 runs, edged and a chance goes down at slip, that would have been the 5-for if he had just held on. **Bihari** has to get to his feet, recover and chase it down before it reaches the ropes.

Panda to **Khan**, 1 run, knocked out past short leg into the midwicket area and **Trahar** runs in from the boundary to collect it.

Panda to **Chancellor**, no run, clipped out towards midwicket, the batswoman wants a run to retain the strike but is sent back by the non-striker. Would have been a very risky single as **Sharma** is quickly around from mid-on to cut it off and get it into the keeper's end.

13:24   England 260-9 after 42 overs.

Shubanka to **Khan**, **caught**, it's top spinning on middle stump, across the left-handed batsman, and it gets a faint outside edge, as the batsman goes to defend it, straight into **Singh**'s gloves, who throws the ball high into the sky in celebration. The team gather in the middle of the square high-fiving and congratulating each other on a very fine bowling performance.

13:24

Mohammed Khan	c. Singh b. Shubanka	3 off 3 balls	FOW: 260 all out

"And that brings an end to the English innings. They finish 260 all out in 42.1 overs. We will take a short break and come back to with India's reply. They need 261 to win."

CHAPTER 6
ENGLAND 260 ALL OUT,
INDIA YET TO BAT, LUNCH INTERVAL

13:30   "Welcome back to Lord's everyone, I'm Patty Pringle and I am joined here in the commentary box by ex-England captain Andy Bird. We are at lunch a little earlier than expected as, for those of you just joining us, England chose to bat and have been bowled out by India without reaching their full over allocation for 260 runs. First over to Ray Dora, our statistics expert for the breakdown of the England innings, and the Indian bowling figures."

"Thanks Patty, England all out for 260 runs in 42.1 overs.

Tom Rhodes, caught and bowled Panda, for 37, England 67 for 1.

Greg Hanson, stumped Singh, bowled Panda, for 4, England 71 for 2.

Ricky Barnes, caught Bihari, bowled Pooran, for 25, England 122 for 3.

Sam King, hit wicket, bowled Pooran, for nought, England 131 for 4.

Alex Quince, bowled Mopal, for 85, England 189 for 5.

Patrick Sherman, bowled Mopal, for 4, England 204 for 6.

Mark Jules, bowled Panda, for 7, England 221 for 7.

William Jones, caught Khan, bowled Shubanka, for 68, England 250 for 8.

Hunter French, bowled Panda, for 2, England 257 for 9.

Mohammed Khan, caught Singh, bowled Shubanka, for 3, England 260 all out.

Sonia Chancellor, not out, for 14 and Extras 11.

Over to the bowlers,

Azer Khan, 8 overs, no maidens, 44 runs, no wickets.

Deepak Pooran, 7 overs, no maidens, 51 runs, 2 wickets.

Nikil Panda, 9 overs, no maidens, 45 runs, 4 wickets.

Varun Mopal, 10 overs, no maidens, 65 runs, 2 wickets.

Shubanka, 7.1 overs, no maidens, 53 runs, 2 wickets.

In terms of the wagon wheel, most of England's runs came on the leg side with just under 40% coming through midwicket, and 10% down to fine leg. This matches up with the bowling as 65% of the scoring deliveries were bowled either on middle stump or down the leg side. After that, the spread was quite even, with 56 runs coming straight, about 20%, and 41 runs through the covers. The Indians in general had a good line, with over 50% of all their deliveries, 139 balls precisely, on or outside off stump. Where they really were consistent however is in the length. As a bowling unit they were disciplined, with over 50% of their deliveries on a good length or just back of a length. If they did err, it was mainly too full, though Panda was the main culprit of this, and you could see that he was trying to flight it up to the batsmen, and got his rewards for doing so. Finally on the fielding front, where we know India have historically struggled, Trahar was the busiest, doing over 20% of the fielding duties alone. Next best was Varun Mopal, who had to put in a full 10 overs while marshalling the boundary rope. Certainly the effort points go to him, alongside his important scalp of Quince. They held onto their chances in the field, taking 4 catches, and just maybe today catches will win matches. Back to you."

"Thank you very much Ray, Andy – what did you make of that English performance?"

"Patty, I'm disappointed, and I know the boys will be too. Some of them had very good starts with both Quince and Billy getting up over 50, though they weren't able to push on from there, nor did they have the support from the other batsman to make a real go of it.

Rhodes and Barnes also got established with scores in the twenties and thirties, but then threw their wickets away. We said at the top of the innings that 300 looked like a good score on this pitch, and whilst we should always caveat that we have only seen one team batting on this pitch so far, 260 certainly feels short. England are going to have an uphill battle as they come out to field, and they will know deep down they are at least 20 runs short."

"Hard to disagree with you, Andy, and they only have themselves to blame. There were some very average shots out there when the situation called for a different style of play. Do you have a word for Sam King?"

"Tough going on debut to be honest. Don't think I have ever seen anything quite like that. For sure he would have been nervous walking out there with the England cap on for the first time, though he has batted a lot on this track before so shouldn't have been caught that much unawares. He will have expected Pooran to come at him with pace and bounce, and should have dealt with it much better than he did. But he is young, this whole series is a learning experience for him, and he will have chances to make amends down the line. There will just be a little bit more pressure on him to take those next chances when they come."

"England called him up because they wanted some solidity in the middle order so they could build to a big score. It has backfired on them?"

"Look, things like that happen in cricket and in sport. It's how you adapt from them that counts. After King was out, Jones looked like he was taking the innings on his shoulders and would have dragged the team up to 300 though mistimed a hittable ball. That ball should have been 20m longer and in the stands, and he knows it. I am especially disappointed in Sherman and Frenchy though: they should have reviewed the situation better than they did when they got out there. Backs against the wall requires a certain type of play, they know they, but failed to execute it."

"Ok thanks Andy, lets now go downstairs to Mike who has busted his way into the Lord's pavilion and who is now with Indian captain

Sunil Sharma."

13:35 "Sunil, hi, tell us what you are thinking right now, good performance by your team?"

"Mike you nailed it. I am really proud of the way the boys have come out this morning and done their business. We bowled tight lines, fielded well and kept the run rate low. It also helped that we were able to take wickets at regular intervals to limit the scoring."

"Tell me about your bowlers, who stood out for you?"

"The boys bowl as a team and as a unit. They work hard together and get the results together. It is hard to pick any one out. Of course, Nikil got the most rewards today with his 4 wickets, but he would equally say that it was the pressure being created around him that helped him to that. Mopal, Pooran and Azer at the start do all the hard yards, beating the batsmen down, so they must be given credit. Azer unfortunately didn't get any wickets today, but he was relentless with the pressure at the top of the order. That's why I kept him going for so long. If he had had a chance to bowl at some of the tail he may have gotten some rewards."

"Are you surprised there was so much for the spinners out there?"

"We expected the ball to turn, that's why we came in with 2 spinners, though I was surprised that they took most of the wickets. I think they got 6 between them, and some big wickets in that too? The pitch was a bit flat but there were some parts where you could get the ball to turn."

"You would have taken 260 at the start of the innings if it was offered to you?"

"For sure, but it is very early in this match yet. We now need to go out there with the bat and chase it down. Certainly we prefer chasing 260 rather than 300, but then we would have also taken a lot less than that too. We now need to be extremely careful with our wickets, not give anything away too easily and take the opportunities where they come. The ground is very big and it is hard to clear the fence. So we need to run hard, and keep the scoreboard ticking over. We have the experience for big games like this throughout the squad and we need to use that now."

"Any changes to the order?"

"No, I don't think so at the moment. Kumar and Kapoor will be leading us off. I have told them to play their natural game. No need to play defensively just because the run rate is a tick over 5. They are more likely to get out playing in an unnatural style then doing what they do best. Bihari will come in behind them, and hopefully if they get all the runs between them, then I will have a very quiet afternoon."

"Thanks Sunil and good luck with the chase. Patty, Sunil and his Indian team are full of confidence, but saying all the right things and not taking anything for granted. They know how ruthless this English bowling attack can be, especially when they are at home in these conditions. They seem cautiously optimistic, and I would expect nothing less. I have now just come across to the other side of the pavilion, where I hope William Jones is waiting for me? Ah, I think he is just in the middle of a team talk at the moment, perhaps I can get a word with Angus. Angus, good afternoon, what do you make of the English performance?"

"Hi Mike, it was tough out there to be sure. The Indians bowled aggressively and tight, didn't give anything away and took wickets at the right time to stem our momentum, and you know how important momentum is in these situations."

"You had some great opportunities?"

"Yes we did, Quince and Jones both played beautifully for their scores, and will be disappointed with not finishing it off. We didn't hold our bottle through the middle of the innings, but that doesn't give enough credit to the bowlers out there, they outperformed us. This being said, they had the conditions in their favour and took advantage, the conditions haven't really changed and now it's our chance to turn the screw. We have posted a score, we will get some scoreboard pressure if we can make some early breakthroughs, and we have the talent to defend this. It is going to be much closer than people think, and the boys are up for winning this game from here."

"You have only come in with one spinner and after seeing how Panda and Shubanka performed on this wicket are you rueing that decision?"

"I don't think so. We have a world class spinner in Chancellor and she will have to prove her stuff today. But don't count out the rest of our attack either. We are nicely balanced with 3 quicks, a spinner and then Sherman who can nibble it around and make the pitch work for him. This is a structure we have had for a while and it is still sensible for English conditions, especially here at Lord's. Normally we would not expect much turn, and so we aren't set up for it, but if conditions change then Jones can always call on Barney to turn over a few overs with his off breaks."

"Thanks Angus and good luck for this afternoon. Patty we couldn't get up to Jones who is still in a huddle with the English boys, though Angus says the boys are up for it, it will be close, and England are going out there for the win. Back to you."

13:45 "Thanks Mike, and interesting thoughts there from Captain Sharma and Angus, the head coach of the England. Now we are going to step away from this game and I am very privileged to be joined in the booth by His Royal Highness the Duke of Exeter. The Duke has had a long history and love of cricket and has been President of the Board of Control for Cricket in England for the last 10 years. In that time cricket has gone through a big resurgence in popularity, a renaissance to a certain extent in the style the game is played and importantly a spread at grass roots level, through schools, clubs and universities in England. In the same period the country has had its fair share of constitutional crises which the Duke has had a front row seat at, and hopefully we can get his thoughts on some of these. If you do have any questions that you would like me to ask him, as always, please send us a message @PPringles and we will do our best in the time we have. Welcome, sir, and thanks for joining us. Firstly to the sport, it's been a good 10 years for English cricket?"

"Thank you Patty, good to be with you, and yes we can say it has been a good period and a good recovery. England won the World

Cup in 19 with lots of fanfare and energy, and that momentum was pricked with a pin the year after with the 2020 lockdown. At the top of the game that lockdown didn't have too much of an effect; the national sides were able to maintain a full calendar, though at county level, at club level and even school level it was a heart attack, just as they were gearing up to capitalise on England's performance. The lockdowns put a lot of counties and clubs into financial difficultly and they were struggling to see a way out. However I am pleased to say that right at the beginning of my term, the BCCE engaged with our sponsors, and the government, got the money into the game and we were able to distribute it quickly, fairly and effectively, which is why the game survived. It was very much an existential crisis that we came through together. On the back of that the game has gotten stronger and stronger. And what I am most pleased about is that it is stronger in all parts of the game, Test matches, One-days and the short forms, T-20s and The Hundred."

"Which is your favourite?"

"I think everyone expects me to be a traditionalist. I am in my 70s, was grounded in cricket before all of these short forms came around, watching the tall West Indians bounce out anyone in their sights, while the Laras and Tendulkars got their massive scores. So I am expected to love Test cricket, and I do. However to put a fly in the ointment, it's actually One-days that pique my interest the most. There is enough time for both sides to put on a show, one or two players on either side could win or lose the game, and you get a result! Like today: someone will win, and someone will lose, and what more could you ask for in sport. Even with the World Test Championship there is not enough competition in Test matches anymore, and there are too many draws or playing for draws. The short forms are lots of fun too, but too much luck and brashness for me. For sure they require skill but the hit out and then get out mentality isn't my cup of tea."

"So you are looking forward the World Cup coming back to England next year?"

"For sure, we at the BCCE are gearing up for it. 19 was such a special tournament, with an incredible final right here at Lord's, 23 in India was like nothing I have ever seen before. The Indian fan base is fanatical and I'm not sure what would have happened if they hadn't won on home soil again. There would have been rioting! Then last time out in the West Indies I was quite surprised that South Africa won, they hadn't come in with much form, though executed the tournament so well and just beat effectively this Indian team, in the final. We bring it back home next year, and hopefully the trophy can stay here!"

"What are you planning differently for that tournament?"

"So much has changed in the game while I have been here at the BCCE, including many of our priorities. Firstly we want the game's show piece event to be much more inclusive than it has been in the past and so while working with the International Cricket Council we have changed the format to have 24 teams in the competition. This will give a bigger chance for the smaller countries and non-traditional cricket countries to have a go and get a feel for what World Cup action is like. To accommodate this we will have to make the tournament a bit longer and we have blocked out a period from just after the IPL finishes until mid-July. Secondly, we will be a bit broader this time in where we stage the games, in order to spread the game around these Islands a bit more. We will hold some games in Ireland, Northern Ireland, and even Scotland, and each of those nations will also have a team at the tournament. Finally, we will be running the Women's World Cup directly before the Men's version in order to continue to build its popularity. Oh wait, I can't say Men's version anymore?"

"No, you cant, as of course women, such as Sonia Chancellor, are allowed to play in it. This will be her first main World Cup along with a few others; are you pleased with the way women have been integrated into the highest level of the sport?"

"We want the best out there showing their skills, whoever they are. That's what makes the spectacle so interesting. You are right: it's not only England, it is likely that Australia will have a couple of ladies in their squad, and some of the smaller nations will combine their men's and women's teams. So we may see up to 10 women get some sort of game next year, and they should be geared up and ready for it, as they will all have just played in their own World Cup just before. What is most pleasing to me is that the BCCE have been leading this effort for more engagement in women's sport and bringing them up to the highest level. There are very talented sportswomen out there, though to get to the top you need support, training, facilities, investment and most importantly competition. 5 years ago we made it compulsory for each county team to have at least 2 women in their match-day squads, and at least 1 on the team sheet. This forced the counties to invest in their development programmes for the women's game and gave them the competition against the best in the sport to improve. I'm proud to have led that change, and that my peers at other cricket boards also took up the mantle and tried similar things. We were the first major sport to do this and we can be proud to have led this change."

13:50 "As you mentioned Scotland in particular, lets now move away from cricket for a couple of minutes and get some of your insight into what has been going on in your family and more importantly with our country in the last few years. Of course there has been lots of discussion all over the airways of the effect that Scotland gaining independence has had on the rest of the UK and the real possibility of a full breakup of the other three nations now, but tell me how have you seen the situation and how is your nephew King William now handling the situation."

"To be honest Patty I am really here to just talk about my role in cricket and its development, though I can say a few words on the topic as you have asked so nicely. I will start with my brother, Charles, who was thrown into leadership by the death of the Queen a few years ago. Of course, he was ready for it and effectively had been waiting 50 years to take the mantle on. What he wasn't ready for however was the political differences at the time and the resentment the 4 nations held against each other. My family have a responsibility for all the people of our nations, and so even though we didn't take a position on the independence vote or its confirmation, it still hurt, and to no one more so than Charles. He wanted to be King of all

4 countries, and the entire commonwealth, and so to be the King that presided over the breakup of the United Kingdom gave him an unwanted place in history. He took it so personally and deeply that he couldn't wear the crown anymore, and so after waiting almost a lifetime for it, passed it down. In that moment I believe he showed unbelievable courage and resolve, and I give him full credit for it. Now as an advisor to William he continues to build on the family legacy and continues the good work he has done for the country over the last 80 years, even if it is a smaller country. William is learning the ropes. He never expected to be in this position so early, though he has broad shoulders and is doing his duty. He is the flag-bearer for the country and the commonwealth now and we must all give him our support and blessings to do as good a job as possible. I have watched him grow into the role nicely though he will have to do it in his own way. The world is very different to when Charles and I were growing up – no internet, no social media, no 24h news, and after the legacy of the Queen the country expects something very different from the Royalty, if it is to survive, and William, Catherine and their children now need to work their way through that."

"Do you think he can bring us together again?"

"Certainly from a philosophical point of view that is his challenge and his goal. Whether it is possible in practise in terms of re-joining the union that lasted for 320 years or indeed even stopping a further break up is, I don't know. Certainly it is not 'up to us' and if the world moves that way, and people want a change then that's the way we will go. William's job now will be to show leadership to make sure that our nations stay culturally as close together as possible, work together, support each other, whilst carving our different paths in the world. For the time being he remains King of Scotland as a separate entity to the United Kingdom, and leader of the Church of Scotland, though if that survives down to George's, or even William's, lifetime I am very uncertain. In the end it is up to all of us to make sure we remain friends, family indeed, and that's what we are doing in cricket. We are forging a path through the pre-eminent sport in the commonwealth to forge stronger ties together, both with nations far away and close by. The World Cup next year will build on that; we will host the tournament jointly with Scotland and Northern Ireland, host matches in Glasgow and Belfast and bring our communities together through top sporting endeavour and achievement."

"Thank you very much, your highness, as always it is a real pleasure to speak to you and get your first-hand insight into a world far above us. We appreciate the candour and openness you have shown us and hope that your plans for the BCCE continue to progress well and indeed England-Scotland 2031 next year is a spectacle and a success. Before you go: who is your money on today, have England scored enough, and can England retake the World Cup next year?"

"Haha, well 260 is a good score, but I fear it will be a bit short. None the less scoreboard pressure always got to me when I was out there batting, albeit at schoolboy level, and here it comes at you from 10 different scoreboards around the ground so it will be hard to avoid. I think India will chase it down, but it is going to be very tight either way. For sure England can be successful next year, but India are doing the right thing in coming over here to get some practise in our conditions. There are smart people over at the Indian Cricket Board, we will have to keep a keen eye on them! It will be an open and competitive tournament no doubt, but lots of cricket to play before then."

13:55 "Indeed, thank you, and as Bobby Jungan comes in to take your place in the booth for the start of the Indian chase I can tell you that England are out on the pitch and have started to run through some stretching and fielding exercises. Sherman, Rhodes and Hanson are playing a quick game of one-touch football whilst all of the bowlers are huddled in the middle of the square, presumably deciding which end they want to bowl from. Bobby, welcome back, how do you see this one playing out, is it enough?"

"Patty, it's a decent score. It wasn't quite as flat as everyone thought it was going to be at the start of the day and England didn't bat badly. Ok, there were some loose shots though Quince and Jones both played quality innings, and have given them something to protect. India historically don't like chasing, they prefer to set a score and then defend it, and so it is very much all to play for. England will start with

Jules and Khan, pace from different angles, and Kumar and Kapoor are going to have to deal with it. Kumar doesn't have a defensive gear and so could go big or could go back into the hutch quickly. If they are both still there are the end of the first spells then they will get this at a canter, if they are 50 for 2 after the first powerplay it is a different story and all to play for."

"Kumar is coming off a purple patch, no?"

"He is not coming off one, he is right in the middle of it. He had a fantastic time in the IPL and was able to lead Goa to the championship with some big hitting straight from the top of the order, whilst also protecting his wicket. April in Downtown Goa is very different to a June afternoon in North London though: the conditions, the temperature and the length of the boundaries, so we will have to see if he has adapted his game enough. He only flew into the country recently, only played in one of the warm up games and has been thrown right into the deep end. At this level that is exactly what is expected of you. 2 billion people in India will want to see results, and will want this chase to be quick and efficient. If you can hit a few into the stands too then that will make everyone a little happier."

"And what about Kapoor?"

"He is a diligent player, defensive and a perfect balance to Kumar. He will nudge it around, rotate the strike, annoy the fielding captain, and has a lot of stickability. He does not give his wicket away easily and will be thinking of how he can bat for 35 overs plus. They have been very successful over the last few years for India, especially since we have gone away from the all-out "bang bang" of ten years ago. Back then they set up with 5 out of the 6 top order batsmen being big hitters, though the bowlers quickly learned how to bowl to them, and the powers-that-be increased the size of the pitches to make it fairer. In the modern game, especially in this format, you need guile and stickability to post a score, or even chase down a score. 5 an over is on the light side so they will have a plan to chase it, keep their heads down and go do their work. Let's see what happens."

"Here they come now, down the pavilion white bleachers and out into the middle, to a massive celebration from the partisan crowd.

They know that we have a game on here, and that India are favourites for it. They will be giving them all the support they can to get them over the line. England have now also taken their positions in the field and as expected it will be Mark Jules to come from the pavilion end to start. Kumar will be facing the first ball and the field is as follows. Quince is behind the stumps, with Jones and Hanson at first and second slip. They have Barnes at gully, Rhodes at point, Sherman at extra cover and French at mid-off. It is a 6-3 field, with Chancellor at mid-on, Khan at fine leg and finally Sam King right under the batsman's nose at short leg. Remember in this first power play England are only allowed 2 outside the 30-yard circle, and they don't even have that it seems. They are going very aggressively here as they know they will have to take wickets to make this a close game, and quickly. Kumar does a quick count of the fielders on both sides of the pitch taking a moment to settle himself and requesting a middle stump guard, which umpire Du Toit kindly obliges. India need 261 to win, here we go."

CHAPTER 7
ENGLAND 260 ALL OUT, INDIA 0-0

14:00 "Umpire du Toit signals play."

Jules to **Kumar**, wide, loosener down the legside to start, and taken nicely by the keeper to get him active and into the action early.

Jules to **Kumar**, no run, straightened up and left alone outside the off stump.

Jules to **Kumar**, 2 runs, pulled off a back of a length but hit high on the bat, it runs out through the midwicket gap and **Chancellor** has to run down the hill to field.

Jules to **Kumar**, no run, short and the batsman ducks out of it in time, no signal from the umpire.

Jules to **Kumar**, 2 runs, full and straight and driven back past the bowler towards the pavilion. **French** catches up to it right in front of the members.

Jules to **Kumar**, 1 run, good line and length and squeezed out into the offside and they take a quick single as **Rhodes** runs around from point to field with his wrong hand.

Jules to **Kapoor**, no run, back of a length and left alone outside the off stump.

14:04 India 6-0 after 1 over. England 7-0, RRR: 5.21. "Mohammed Khan, the left arm seamer, will come on from the Nursery End, bowling left arm over the wicket. The field is similar, though the gully has been taken out and moved to third man, and Sherman at extra cover has come into a catching position at short cover."

Khan to **Kumar**, 1 leg bye, first ball is back of a length and down the legside, though angling into the batsman and it hits his leg as he tries to clip it away. It is fielded by **Jules** at fine leg.

Khan to **Kapoor**, no run, back of a length and straighter, left alone whilst covering up the stumps.

Khan to **Kapoor**, wide, outside the off stump and swinging away from the batsman. There is plenty of movement down the hill there though it swings wide enough that it has to be taken at 2nd slip and it is called a wide by **Umpire Randall**, without too much thought.

Khan to **Kapoor**, no run, on the stumps and defended solidly out to short leg.

Khan to **Kapoor**, 2 runs, on the pads and deflected past an outstretched short leg for 2 as **Jules** has to run around from fine leg to field on the square leg boundary, in front of the Grandstand.

Khan to **Kapoor**, 1 run, on the pads again and glanced fine down to **Jules** at fine leg and they jog through for only a single. The umpires have called an end to the over there, but certainly there should be one more ball? **Randall** didn't give much thought to the wide itself and then promptly forgot about it.

14:08   India 11-0 after 2 overs. England 12-0, RRR: 5.21.

Jules to **Kapoor**, 2 runs, straight ball but a little short and pulled across down the hill towards the midwicket boundary. **Chancellor** was expecting the shot and was quick off her mark at mid-on to get down there and cut of the boundary.

Jules to **Kapoor**, no run, outside the off stump and watched as it passes through to the keeper, bat nicely out of the way.

Jules to **Kapoor**, 1 run, guided down along the floor towards the slips but **Hanson** at second slip gets a diving hand to it and slows it down, **Barnes** chases it down as they get through for a single on the misfield.

Jules to **Kumar**, 1 run, defended out into the legside and **King** has to swivel and chase it out across the square.

Jules to **Kapoor**, no run, in-swinging yorker which is just stopped by the batsman slamming the bat down and jumping to get his feet out of the way, nice delivery which allows **Jules** to give the batsman a lingering stare.

Jules to **Kapoor**, 2 runs, the pressure doesn't last long as the next one is too full and driven straight past the non-striker and **Chancellor** collects it before it runs into the boundary in front of the pavilion.

14:12   India 17-0 after 3 overs. England 15-0, RRR: 5.19.

Khan to **Kumar**, no run, back of a length and left alone outside the off stump.

Khan to **Kumar**, 6 runs, short delivery and picked up early and hooked off the middle of the bat high into the air and it lands 10 rows back in the Grandstand in the middle of an Indian crowd contingent.

Khan to **Kumar**, 6 runs, tries to correct and goes too full on leg stump this time, the batsman gets his foot out of the way and drives the half volley flat and long over mid-on and just over the long boundary rope in front of the Media Centre.

Khan to **Kumar**, 1 run, tries to hook it again but it's not really short enough and can only get the end of the bat to flick it in the air out towards fine leg where **Jules** collects it on the first bounce.

Khan to **Kapoor**, 2 runs, good ball but better shot as it is driven squarish past short cover down the hill and **Rhodes** who is very quick dives to haul it in and prevent the boundary, while **Sherman** throws it in.

Khan to **Kapoor**, no run, left alone outside the line, directed towards 2nd slip, but not called a wide this time.

"Bobby, wow, big over from Kumar, starting to find his straps early in this one?"

"It took him a couple of overs to get his eye in though he is seeing this white ball like a football and giving the bad balls the treatment they deserve. Two big hits from the man in form and as we expected he is taking it to the bowlers here, throwing the pressure right back on them. As I said at the top, he doesn't have a slow gear and has the ability to win games all by himself. On the other hand Kapoor is letting him do his stuff and will take a back seat while the show is going on. Mo Khan hasn't found his rhythm yet and with so few runs on the scoreboard that will annoy the captain. He needs to be threatening from ball one, but has let go 19 runs in 2 overs. Jules on the other hand has looked better, still leaking runs though has a field set to take wickets, which was never going to be economical. If he can strike then it will have been worth it."

13:59 **Vikas @V4India:** @PPringles Ok its go time boys!! Chaaaakadey India

14:00 **Geoff @barmyGeoff:** @PPringles @barmy1992 Jules needs to step up with a big opening spell here. Get these openers back in the hutch

14:02 **Craig @barmy1992:** *replying to @barmyGeoff* @jules_england and @MoKduck need to bring it! Pace and bounce boys!

14:02 **Jon Knight @SirJon:** @PPringles Completely agree with @jungan_cricket this is going to be a close one, but only if England get some wickets early.

14:04 **toby @Tobytools:** @PPringles @SirJon What is this field for, Jules? They need wickets for sure, but there are so many gaps!

14:06 **kiks @nikita_aol:** @PPringles India are going to coast to this total with extras! If @MokDuck doesn't find his lines quickly @billythekid is going to have a bowling problem

14:10 **Craig @barmy1992:** @PPringles @barmyGeoff OH that was a demon ball from Jules! I felt the icy stare from here! That boy can move it around corners!

14:11　**kiks @nikita_aol:** @PPringles Oi ref! where is the extra ball for the over?? @BCCElive these umpires are biased!

14:12　**Geoff @barmyGeoff:** *replying to @barmy1992* Haha, pressure didn't last long. @glassceiling100 is looking fine in the field today!

14:13　**toby @Tobytools:** *replying to @barmyGeoff* oh yes indeed friend!

14:14　**Vikas @V4India:** @PPringles BOOM BOOM here we go! Catching practise in the Grandstand!

14:15　**kiks @nikita_aol:** *replying to @V4India* And down the ground! SMAASH!

14:16　**Craig @barmy1992:** @PPringles get your act together @MoKduck! We have paid for a full game of cricket!

14:17　**toby @Tobytools:** *replying to @barmy1992* Its all fixed mate! @MoKduck is probably on the Indian payroll! What happened to the British talent @BCCElive?

14:17　India 32-0 after 4 overs. England 26-0, RRR: 4.98.

"**Jules** to **Kapoor**, 1 run, defended straight to mid-off, though **French** is right on the edge of the circle and they can get a quick single.

Jules to **Kumar**, no run, straight and defended out to point.

Jules to **Kumar**, 1 run, short delivery cut into the ground and stopped by a one-handed dive towards backward point by **Rhodes**, **Barnes** catches does the clean-up work from gully.

Jules to **Kapoor**, no run, short and bodyline, fended off to short leg on tip toes.

Jules to **Kapoor**, 1 run, on the pads and clipped down to **Khan** at fine leg.

Jules to **Kumar**, 2 runs, driven on the front foot up the hill and into the covers. **Rhodes** and **Sherman** work together on the cover boundary to catch up to it and haul it in.

14:21 India 37-0 after 5 overs. England 33-0, RRR: 4.98. "Khan is changing to left arm around the wicket."

Khan to **Kapoor**, no run, better line from around the wicket, back of a length and defended out to point.

Khan to **Kapoor**, 2 runs, drifts onto the pads and too short, it is pulled out into the legside but not from the middle of the bat. **Chancellor** fields from mid-on as the ball is rolling towards the Compton stand.

Khan to **Kapoor**, no run, middle line and back of a length, but swinging back into the batsman and it is defended out into the leg side.

Khan to **Kapoor**, 4 runs, just drifting out on the pads on a good length, and is clipped very fine off the middle of the bat and it races to the pavilion boundary as **Jules** tries to make a dive.

Khan to **Kapoor**, 2 runs, driven off the front foot of too full a length past **Sherman** who has to chase it down the hill.

Khan to **Kapoor**, 2 runs, these are becoming too easy for the batsmen now, too full a length again on off stump and driven down the ground. The batsman will be disappointed more of these are not finding the boundary, but the straight boundary is very long and **French** can chase it in.

14:26 India 47-0 after 6 overs. England 39-0, RRR: 4.86.

Jules to **Kumar**, no run, back of a length and swinging away towards the slips and left alone.

Jules to **Kumar**, 2 runs, full delivery swinging in though not quite yorker length and gets driven back past the bowler, who gets a hand to it to slow it down, though still requires some chasing from **Chancellor**.

Jules to **Kumar**, 4 runs, big shot back over the bowler's head, straight as an arrow and flat, one bounce and it is over the boundary in front of the members sitting in the pavilion. This brings up the 50 for India in just 6.3 overs. Their current run rate is 8.15. The batsmen meet in the middle to share a quick fist bump and conversation as the Indian crowd goes ecstatic and bursts into full song. There is also a round of applause from both pavilion balconies where the players dressing rooms are, certainly the right-hand away dressing room giving an ovation with a lot more energy.

Jules to **Kumar**, no run, full delivery, but gets the yorker right this time and it has to be stubbed down underneath the batsman's nose with a little dance to get the toes out of the way.

Jules to **Kumar**, **caught**, and it's a surprise shorter delivery which kicks off the surface and is well directed right into the midriff of the batsman, he tries to fend it off down into the legside though it hits glove and pops up towards the short mid-on area. **King** is quick off his toes at short leg takes a step and then a full outstretched dive back towards the bowler to catch it a foot off the ground with his left hand. England have the breakthrough.

14:29

| Ravi Kumar | c. King b. Jules | 30 off 22 balls | FOW: 53-1 |

"Bobby, that's the wicket England needed. Kumar was just getting started and was already up to a rapid 30, showing no fear and slapping it all around the ground, but now he is heading back to the pavilion."

"Patty, the whole stadium has just fallen silent. It's eerie and shocking. The Indians were in a boisterous mood both through lunch as they knew this was a chase-able score and even more so given the way Ravi came out and took the game right to the English opening bowlers. The two big hits out of the ground had fired up the supporters and now there is stunned silence. This is just what Jules will have been looking for and exactly why the captain was willing to give him some flexibility in his field settings. That change of length; full, full, full, then banged in short, surprised the batsman and he had no choice but to try and fend it off. It was expertly targeted right into the chest, no chance to duck under it, and that's what the short leg is there for."

"It was a fantastic catch by the young man under the helmet, diving with his left hand. I think he may have even redeemed himself for his batting performance. Certainly his team know just how valuable that catch is. Do you think England will continue with this aggressive strategy?"

"It was a great catch, though I think he still needs a couple more to redeem himself for that first innings dismissal. I had to watch it a few times to figure out just what went on, very unusual in this day and age to hit your own stumps! He must have been very nervous. Anyway, I think England have to continue this strategy. They have to force the pace and try and take wickets. If India are allowed to settle in and knock it around into gaps they will stroll to the total. I think they will give Mo a break though. It looks like French is stretching and warming up to come on at his end. Khan just hasn't found his rhythm this morning in those first few overs, and to be fair Kapoor was hitting him around just as much as Kumar. Give him a break to reset himself and then maybe he can come back during the second powerplay."

"Next we have Ankit Bihari coming out to bat and making the long walk across to take guard at the nursery end. He will have only one more ball to face from Jules who is waiting patiently at the top of his mark, throwing the ball out to Sonia and trying to keep loose. Ankit takes a middle stump guard showing 2 fingers to Umpire du Toit and sets himself."

Jules to **Bihari**, 2 runs, on pads and back of a length, guided into the open midwicket space and **King** has to chase behind him across the square to collect it, but these two are quick between the wickets.

14:33   India 55-1 after 7 overs. England 44-0, RRR: 4.79. "As Bobby predicted, Hunter French is coming on to replace Khan from the Nursery End. The short leg has come out and moves to extra cover, there is a big gap through midwicket."

French to **Kapoor**, no run, good opening delivery, outside off stump and left alone by the batsman.

French to **Kapoor**, 2 runs, just drifted too straight and clipped off the pads into that vacant legside gap. **Chancellor** runs around from mid-on to field.

French to **Kapoor**, no run, short and outside the off stump, the batsman thought about a swing for a second, before throwing his arms up and away from the ball.

French to **Kapoor**, 2 runs, short and outside the off stump again, this time it's guided past point through the gully region, and **Barnes** runs around from 3rd man to collect it.

French to **Kapoor**, 1 run, batsman dances down the wicket and makes a full ball into a full toss and it is pushed into the offside past short cover. **King** comes around from extra cover with some acrobatics to stop a certain boundary.

French to **Bihari**, 2 runs, a little too straight and the batsman gets far enough across the off stump to deflect it out through square leg. **Jules** fields on the square leg boundary from fine leg. Expensive first over, and not much difference from **Khan.**

14:38   India 62-1 after 8 overs. England 49-0, RRR: 4.74.

Jules to **Kapoor**, no run, outside the off stump, a little short and left alone.

Jules to **Kapoor**, no run, back of a length and swinging away from the batsman, good ball and the fielding team know it.

Jules to **Kapoor**, 4 runs, it's a great delivery, swinging away from off stump. Unluckily the batsman gets a thick edge as he tries to drive hard at it, and it goes through the gap in the field at 4th slip in the air. The speed of the delivery easily takes it down to the boundary. The entire team has their hands on their heads.

Jules to **Kapoor**, 2 runs, straight delivery with not much movement, clipped off the pads as short leg shields himself from getting hit, and it is collected at the bottom of the hill by **Chancellor**.

Jules to **Kapoor**, 1 run, full delivery stamped out slowly to mid-off and they can take a quick single as **Khan** tries a shy at the stumps and misses.

Jules to **Bihari**, 2 runs, steps out across the off stump again and clips it away through square leg for another couple of runs as **French** fields at deep square leg.

14:43   India 71-1 after 9 overs. England 53-0, RRR: 4.63.

French to **Kapoor**, no run, outside the off stump, back of a length without much movement and left alone by the batsman.

French to **Kapoor**, **appeal stumped**, the batsmen charges at the ball a little to try and reach it, but can't quite get there, **Quince** takes an underarm shy at the stumps from 10 yards away and hits it, giving a muffled unconvincing appeal. The appeal from point is a little stronger, though **Umpire du Toit** isn't that interested, however it looks like we are going to go upstairs for an umpire review, the soft signal on the pitch is not out.

"Umpire to TV director, we have an umpire review for stumping, please can we please check the no-ball line first. Yes, it seems ok. Now can I have the side on view of the stumps please. The batsman is standing outside of the popping crease, he plays at the ball, wait for it, wait for it, here comes the ball now, and there it hits the stumps. That's not a good angle, we cannot see where the batsman is, can I please have a view of the stumps and the batsman together? Ok the batsman is stretching back for the line now, can you please zoom in? Ok and his bat is up, up, up, now it's down, and the bails are already in the air. I'll have a look from the other side now to check, yes the ball hits there and the bat is above the ground by inches, it is out. Umpire du Toit you can change your decision, it is out."

14:47

Rohan Kapoor	st. Quince b. French	32 off 32 balls	FOW: 71-2

"That's come out of nowhere Bobby, England have the 2 openers out, one in very strange circumstances and this game is ebbing and flowing like a yo-yo?"

"Patty we can't take our eyes off the action at the moment. Kapoor heads back in complete shock. He has been playing outside his crease and was trying to take the game to the new bowler sort of charging at him. He never in one hundred games would have thought the keeper would take a shy at the stumps and knock them over before he got back in. Everyone was shocked, Quince didn't really even appeal, but it was the appeal from Rhodes at point that convinced du Toit to go upstairs, and he was vindicated. This is exactly what England needed, a bit of good luck and in hindsight a good change of bowling. We said this game would get very interesting if India were 2 down before the 10 overs, and that's where we are. They have built a big foundation through, 71 off 9 overs, and so I think this game is very evenly poised at the moment, perhaps a bit in India's favour on the win predicter but not by much?"

"Captain Sharma is the next man into the middle and has a big weight on his shoulders now. He needs to marshal this Indian team for the next 20 overs to make sure they consolidate wickets and have enough in hand to make a big push towards the end of the innings. Slowing the run rate down to 2 or 3 an over wouldn't be a problem?"

"You have said it perfectly; he has a big innings to play here and he shouldn't worry about boundaries or anything big in the next 10 overs. Just survive for this period and give yourself enough wickets in hand to turn up the heat at the end to get to 261. If I was out there I would play the next 10 overs as a test match, try and get to the 20th over perhaps 110 or 120 for 2 or at worst 3. Take the innings in small workable chunks and plan your way of getting there. He shouldn't be distracted by the low target score, there is still a lot of time in this match."

"He walks out to the middle now and Quince and Jones standing behind the stumps give him a little smirk and a comment as he walks past, and this seem like a good time as any for us to go down to Jones on the pitch! We have him plugged in to our coverage and we can now turn on his captain's microphone which he has kindly worn while in the field. William I hope you can hear me, can you give us your take on the game so far?"

"Hi Patty, yes can hear you clearly, may need to turn it down a bit to be honest! The game is nicely set, great piece of work there by Quince, really quick thinking. I didn't think it was out, but the tv review doesn't lie. Two dangerous batsmen down, we are right into the game now."

"And that catch from King, has he redeemed himself?"

"It was a great catch. The whole world seemed to stand still while the ball was in the air and then he jumps out of nowhere to take a stunner. It will give him real confidence but there is no redemption needed, he was extremely unlucky earlier, and now he has a job to do in the field to get us over the line. Kumar is a big scalp, he has been on top form of late and we are glad to see the end of him."

"What were you saying to Sharma as he came past you there?"

"Haha, not for publication, lucky the mike wasn't on then. Pretty much the same thing he said to me when I came out to bat, nice to see you mate and aren't you here a bit early? Something to get him thinking. We have a good relationship – we both fight hard for our teams when we are out here, but happy to take it less seriously off the pitch, have to enjoy our time as captains."

"What's your strategy for him?"

"Give me a second."

French to **Sharma**, 2 runs, swatted off his pads out towards the grandstand boundary, though stopped by **Chancellor**.

"Bowling bowling Frenchy!! Let's keep it there, keep him playing at it. Well in Sonia, good save! .. Patty, I can't tell you all my plans for him, he may hear them! But we have some plans now that he is in! He is strong outside the off stump and likes pace on the ball, so we will try not to do too much of that. He is a class batsman, so hopefully we can get him out of here quickly without troubling the scorers too much."

"Would you take this position if you had been offered it after 10 overs?"

French to **Sharma**, no run, defended outside the off stump out to **Rhodes** at point."

"Fielding, Rhodes, bowling Frenchy! Keep it there! Get it in quick boys, lets smother them. No easy runs. Patty, are you still there?, um .. I'm not sure. We have given away a lot of runs already and don't have that many to play with. I think I would have taken this situation, 70 odd for 2 with two new batsmen at the crease, rather than 70 odd, with a 50 run partnership still going. When these two get runs, they tend to get big runs quickly. Who knows, this is where we are. Sonia, Sonia .. warm up – pavilion end, next."

French to **Sharma**, no run, back of a length and left alone outside the off stump.

"Ah so we know what's coming up next, turning to spin?"

"No no, Sonia is going to bowl some pacey bouncy stuff! Bounce out these boys, they won't see it coming! To be fair she can get that arm over quickly when she wants too, her quick ones are up in the high 70s anyway. Darts! Tight now boys, don't give away anything."

French to **Sharma**, 1 run, clipped off the pads down to **Jules** at fine leg.

14:53 India 74-2 after 10 overs. England 59-0, RRR: 4.68. "That's the end of the 1st powerplay and the voice you are hearing is our onfield correspondent, England captain William Jones, who has now brought Sonia Chancellor, the leg spinner into the attack. We will give them a couple of minutes to reset their field given that they can now have 4 fielders outside the 30 yard circle and in the meantime go to Jon Knight, an ex-England captain, who has taken Bobby Jungan's place with me in the booth. Jon, thoughts on the match so far?"

"It's going to be pretty close which will be exciting. Can't really tell which way it is going to go at the moment. The runs required number on all those scoreboards around the ground can loom large in a batting team's mind's eye. They still need 180 odd in 40 overs? Seems simple enough on paper, but this game isn't played in a book!"

"Is Sonia coming on too early here?"

"They have had to change all their plans as Mo hasn't been getting it done. Hasn't looked his normal ruthless self and has been very expensive. The captain had a little rethink, brought Frenchy on a bit earlier than he would have wanted too, and at the other end has to give Jules a break. Especially if he wants him fresh later on in the innings, he isn't a young man anymore. The powerplay is over so Sonia can get a bit of protection around the ground, so why not give her a chance? The Indian spinners got the job done very effectively, and she has spent the last few months learning all of their tricks and from their expertise. On the other hand, Sharma has seen a lot of her in the last few months. He should know all her variations, but hopefully she has kept something back."

"So the field is set up for Sonia Chancellor and as expected they have put up an in-out field. Men on the boundary at square leg, at deep extra cover and straight at deep mid-on and deep mid-off. They still have a slip in place and King has taken his place at short leg again. Going around the infield, keeper, slip, wide short 3rd man, extra cover, short leg and short fine leg. Do we still have you William? What's your thinking here with the bowling change?"

"Yes Patty, still here, .. go round … wider … keep going round, cow corner … Sorry, yep here, just checking the field. Into the 2nd powerplay and it's time for some spin. Sonia has been doing the business for us in the last few matches and stepped up her game in the IPL. Lots of opportunity to put these boys under some pressure even though these Indians think they are handy against spin..."

"Oi Oi! Get ready for some catching practise in the Grandstand more like!!"

"Ok, that was Sunil. I'll be off now, catch up with you guys in a little while."

"Thanks William, funny, with some extra charm there from Captain Sharma too. Ok here we go with Sonia."

Chancellor to **Sharma**, no run, flighted delivery on middle, not much turn, defended to short leg.

Chancellor to **Sharma**, no run, flighted outside the off stump and left alone by the batsman.

Chancellor to **Sharma**, 1 run, too full and driven down the ground for an easy single, where **French** fields and get it back into the bowler's end.

Chancellor to **Bihari**, no run, front foot defence stretching far outside his crease and smothering the ball back to the bowler.

Chancellor to **Bihari**, no run, on middle and got the ball to turn away to a 5th stump line and into the keeper's gloves.

Chancellor to **Bihari, stumped**, beautiful delivery, flighted and enticed the batsman forward, he steps out to try and smother it but it turns sharply towards 1st slip and the keeper takes it and takes the bails off in one swift motion. There is a massive appeal from the bowler, keeper, slip, which also sets off the rest of the team, towards **Umpire Randall**, who doesn't need to review it and gives it out. The batsman already knows without looking at the umpire and continues his forward defensive shot straight back towards the pavilion.

14:58

| Ankit Bihari | st. Quince b. Chancellor | 6 off 6 balls | FOW: 75-3 |

CHAPTER 8
ENGLAND 260 ALL OUT, INDIA 75-3

15:00   India 75-3 after 11 overs. England 67-0, RRR 4.77. "Jon this game has swung solidly in England's favour here, both openers and Bihari are out, and whilst India have stayed ahead of the required run rate the have lost three key wickets."

"Very much so. At the start of this innings we said that this was a very chasable total as long as the Indians kept their heads and managed their way through the innings. Required rate of 5 runs an over at the start, now down below even that is comfortable at this level and they would have expected to coast there. With that wicket, Trahar comes to the crease, and he and the captain have a very tough ask ahead of them to make this a respectable chase. I would say that this is now England's to lose and those 180 or so runs pending are going to weigh very heavily on this batting team. At the moment India's win predictor is around 30% I guess, down from 60% at the start? That's what losing wickets does."

"At the start of the day this pitch was meant to be a road, flat and unsurprising. It has been quite the opposite. Unpredictable and giving the bowling side plenty of action?"

"We saw exactly that with the England innings. They were expecting it to be flat and chose to bat to post a score. In those first 10 overs, which were very well-managed by Rhodes and Quince, they looked like a big score was coming. But then the scoring rate dried up and the wickets started mounting. There were some poor shots though we have to give some credit to the bowlers too. That's exactly what we have to do here: give full marks to England. Not just the bowlers though but also Quince who has been very active and smart behind the stumps and has 2 scalps to show for it. In the first few overs it seemed like India were going to have it all their way, but the next few batsmen will be very tentative and scared coming out here, and will feel the full weight of the scoreboard."

"Well next out is S K Trahar who has had some experience in these tight situation and in these conditions. He batted a bit higher in the order for South London in last year's Hundred, and he will be happy that he got some time at the crease in the London derby here. These are different circumstances though. No need for heroics or big hitting, just preserve your wicket?"

"Yes, that's exactly what Sharma is telling him right now. These two have a job to do if India want to get back into this match. They will need to bat for the next 20 overs or so and try and put another 80 to 100 runs on the boards. That's enough. That will give them the last 15 to get up to the required score, and they have plenty of hitters down the line to get that done. They just need to preserve wickets and the runs will come. Sharma is an expert tactician in that way and that's why he has been so successful. He will have to lead by example here and hope that he doesn't run out of partners before they mount their big finish."

"Sharma will be facing the next delivery as the wicket was taken off Sonia's last delivery. French will continue from the Nursery end and England sensing an opportunity here are keeping their aggressive field. Only 2 fielders remain on the boundary, at 3rd man and fine leg, with 2 slips and a short cover in catching positions. Space on the legside up that hill towards the Grandstand."

French to **Sharma**, 2 runs, drifting down the leg side and clipped very fine up towards the pavilion. **Jules** has to run around from wide fine leg to recover but can't stop the second.

French to **Sharma**, no run, good line and length outside off stump and defended.

French to **Sharma**, 4 runs, full delivery and smashed back over the umpire's head and is over the rope in front of the Media Centre after one bounce. The batsman didn't need to move.

French to **Sharma**, 1 run, back of a length and defended slowly out to mid-on with soft hands, enough for them to get through for a single before **Khan** can get the ball into the keeper.

French to **Trahar**, no run, short-pitched bouncer rising over the ducking batsman, not enough for a wide.

French to **Trahar**, 2 runs, tries the yorker but it is a full toss on middle and guided out into the legside. The batsmen are quick between the wickets and take 2 before **Chancellor** can get around from mid-on.

15:05   India 84-3 after 12 overs. England 71-2, RRR 4.66.

Chancellor to **Sharma**, 2 runs, short and wide outside the off stump, cut away in the covers and **Hanson** runs around to collect it at the point boundary.

Chancellor to **Sharma**, no run, flighted delivery pitching on middle with some turn defended out to short leg.

Chancellor to **Sharma**, 1 run, driven straight past the bowler to **French** at deep mid-off for a jogging single.

Chancellor to **Trahar**, 2 runs, short and wide, guided past the slip fielder down towards the Compton Stand and **Jules** chases after it, with a dive before it hits the fence. Should have been three but the batsmen were jogging as they thought it was going to be four.

Chancellor to **Trahar**, no run, similar type of ball but a bit straighter and can only be defended stoutly by the batsman.

Chancellor to **Trahar**, 2 runs, bad ball to finish the over, on leg stump with no turn and it is hit past a shielding short leg out into cow corner. **Sherman** is quick on the legside and stops the boundary. Expensive over with little risk taken.

15:09   India 91-3 after 13 overs. England 78-2, RRR 4.6.

French to **Sharma**, 1 run, short and into the ribs, defended out into the legside and **Chancellor** fields at midwicket.

French to **Trahar**, no run, bouncer over the short batsman, who sways out the way of it, keeping his bat very clear away from the ball.

French to **Trahar**, 4 runs, bouncer attempted again though it is not strong enough and only medium-paced. It is pulled away from in front of his nose out forward of square leg and into the Grandstand fence.

French to **Trahar**, no run, nice reply, straighter and on a good length, left alone by the batsman and watched back into the keeper's gloves.

French to **Trahar**, 1 run, it's a chance put down in the slips, got the batsman driving and gets the edge off a good length, **Hanson** has a dive to his right though can only get fingers to the ball, and the batsmen get through for a single on the mis-field.

French to **Sharma**, 6 runs, the pressure of the edge and the drop catch evaporates immediately as the ball is pitched up and smashed confidently back over the bowler's head and into the Edrich stand, 5 rows back. The ball was sent very high into the sky and seemed to be up there for ever while the batsman held his pose for the cameras until the ball was in the stands. That is the hundred up for India and the batsman shake hands in the middle.

15:14   India 103-3 after 14 over. England 82-2, RRR 4.39. "Listeners, I am pleased to welcome a special guest into the studio with Jon and I, and the timing couldn't be better. Just as Sunil Sharma tries to steady the ship down the in the middle, we have Priyanka Levante, global ambassador for the Levante group, joining us up here. Not only is she the Global ambassador for Levante, she is a world-famous Bollywood actress, a UNICEF ambassador, and together with Sharma probably the most recognisable couple in India. Priyanka thanks for joining us. I say steady the ship, but that one almost reached us up here in the Media Centre, how do you feel when Sunil is out there?"

"Thanks for having me Patty, hi Jon, it is my pleasure to talk to you both and hello to all the fans out there. To be honest he doesn't let me watch when he is batting! He already has 2 billion people watching him in India and doesn't want the added pressure I guess. Crazy guy doesn't even get me a ticket to the games! That was a great shot but he has to be careful. All day batsmen have been throwing away their wickets cheaply. He needs to concentrate and be there at the end."

"To be honest Priyanka, I certainly wouldn't let my better half watch me doing my current day job! I didn't like when she watched me bat either, it was weird. But I at least offered her a ticket! I guess 1 million viewers plus one is very different from 2 billion and one. How did you get in here today?"

"Well of course he knows I am in London, but I have enough work commitments of my own that I haven't really seen him since he got here. He has been holed up inside the team bubble and focusing on this series. Regarding how I got in? My father and the Levante corporation are supporting this whole series so I was able to scrounge some access without too many problems."

"You say scrounge, but I guess you are not down in the cheap seats?"

"Are there any cheap seats at Lord's anymore? But no, luckily the company has a box where we are entertaining some clients. Shame we couldn't bring them up here to the Levante Media Centre, apparently putting your name on it doesn't give you as much access as you would think. I had to be invited in and escorted up like a prisoner!"

"What do you think of the game so far?"

"It is 50-50 I think at the moment. England batted well at the start but completely collapsed at the end. India haven't started very well and Sunil and SK have work to do. There are still plenty of overs left in this game and they only need 4 an over? It should be straight forward if they can stay out there. It's all good hitting it out of the park, the fans love that but if you get caught doing it you will look very silly. And if you do anything bad then social media can get pretty angry as you know!"

Chancellor to **Trahar**, no run, middle stump line and defended out to short leg.

Chancellor to **Trahar**, 1 run, flighted delivery defended out into the legside and **King** from short leg gets up quickly and catches up to it before it gets off the square.

Chancellor to **Sharma**, no run, quicker delivery catches the batsman by surprise and he has to jab his bat down in defence in front of his pads.

Chancellor to **Sharma**, 1 run, driven softly down to **Khan** at deep mid-on and they jog a single through.

Chancellor to **Trahar**, 2 runs, comes down the pitch and hits it on the full out through midwicket. **Sherman** has to run around and protect the boundary, while **Khan** coming from the other side helps him get the throw-in quickly to prevent the third.

Chancellor to **Trahar**, no run, spinning away towards slip and left alone by the batsman.

15:18   India 107-3 after 15 overs. England 85-2, RRR: 4.4. "Priyanka, we know you have been pushing for more rights for women in India and for women to have a bigger role in society outside of the traditional, how has Sonia helped that?"

"She has been a game-changer. Not only her though, all of the women who have been making the step up from the women's game into the main spotlight. In the UK, Australia, USA, women's sport and women's cricket have been catching up to the men's game in terms of entertainment, excitement and ability. In India however there is still a big separation. Sonia coming into the English county set up, then into the England national team, and most importantly getting into the Mumbai IPL team has changed the perception of that completely. Indian women, not only cricketers, have been empowered by her. She got more publicity in India than Sunil during the IPL and that is saying something! There are a billion Indian women willing her on, from young girls to old grandmothers. They know she is breaking through ceilings for them and their future daughters. She is a true inspiration."

"She has a lot of fans in India, but a lot of opposition too?"

"Of course, there are many in India who think she shouldn't be there, and we are fighting every day to change that perception. They don't understand that talent is talent. There will always be haters, but hopefully in the future those will be because she is playing for the opposition rather than because of who she is. Sunil and I got to know her very well when she was down in Mumbai. In particular we were able to give her some advice on how to handle her new celebrity status. Cricketers are not really famous here, most could walk down the street without attracting any attention, though in India they have to have 24h protection whenever they leave the house. Everyone wants a photo, autograph, or a piece of the clothing you are wearing! It's dangerous. In terms of her specific status, she has strong broad shoulders to carry us all on. She knows the responsibility she has in India and how many millions of girls are looking up to her and counting on her to survive and prosper. Many of them might be supporting England today just because of her."

"And the state of women's cricket in India, how is that developing?"

"To be honest it is hard for me to say, because I don't have the details that the ICB will know. Numbers of girls playing, success rates, engagements etc. I know that many of the Indian women's team have become like actress celebrities on Instagram, which is good for exposure, though I don't know if that translates to the progress in the game. We perform well in World Cups etc, but that is the top 20-30 players in the country. I'm sure they are enjoying themselves and are well looked after. But I don't know how the structure, support and set up is below that, but I would guess we have a lot of work to do. It certainly isn't as well structured as the men's or boy's game. Levante Corporation is trying to help grassroots sports in India for all genders though it is a struggle. People don't have time to play or enough facilities close to their homes, especially girls. I'm glad that they are now expected to go to school, but after that they have chores and work to do at home. That doesn't leave a lot of time for hitting sixes in the park."

"Very interesting and of course we appreciate everything that Levante is doing for our sport. Coming back to this game do you think there will be a good battle between Sonia and Sunil?"

"They have played a lot together in Mumbai and all-around India while travelling, so I guess they should know each other's games very well? English conditions are different though and it is harder for a spinner. But this is home for her, so she should know how to bowl best here? I would have to give the edge to Sunil, if only to avoid getting hate mail on my Instagram!"

French to **Sharma**, 1 run, clipped off the legs down to **Jules** at fine leg.

French to **Trahar**, 4 runs, driven off the front foot down the hill through the covers, expertly timed and no one is stopping that from the boundary.

French to **Trahar**, no run, back of a length and rising, left alone by the batsman. The bowler gives him a stare in frustration.

French to **Trahar**, 4 runs, short ball pulled away square of the wicket using the pace on the ball. Its up in the air, but there is no one around, and after one bounce it hits the fence in front of the Grandstand.

French to **Trahar**, no run, full but very wide, he was trying to get the batsman to drive and bring the slip into play.

French to **Trahar**, no run, well directed short delivery under the helmet and the batsman has to jump to get on top of the ball and defend it down back to the bowler, who is running in hot and angry after an expensive over.

15:23 India 116-3 after 16 overs. England 93-2, RRR: 4.26. "We will go to a drinks break now, but we still have Priyanka Levante here in the booth with Jon Knight and myself, Patty Pringle. Priyanka, tell us what is next for you, and are the rumours circulating true?"

"Well I can't say I know exactly what rumours you are talking about but if you are talking about wedding bells then no not just yet. I told Sunil we could think about it if he won the IPL, but Mumbai didn't even qualify for the playoffs. I'm not going to marry a loser, so he better step it up. Maybe we can make another agreement for if he wins the World Cup next year? I have plenty on my plate at the moment though. As I said I am in London for the summer working on a new movie which should come out next year. It is a dramatic look back at the last 10 years and how India, and the world, has changed since all those restrictions and lockdowns were imposed because of Coronavirus. I am also working with for my father on rolling out the Levante's Global Foundation for supporting impoverished children. So, no time for a wedding right now."

"Are you confirming that he asked? That would be a real scoop for us!"

"Haha .. um .. maybe. That should send the twitterazzi into a frenzy. Luckily Sunil doesn't carry his phone on him when he is playing so he won't see any of it until he gets back to the hotel. Probably won't even know I am here."

"I think the cameras already found you at lunch time Priyanka, so unless he completely missed you on all the Lord's big screens then he probably knows. Hopefully it's not too distracting as you say he has a big job still to do. Thank you very much for joining us and good luck to you and the Levante foundation, and thanks for supporting this nice and cosy Media Centre for us, hope to see you again soon. Jon, Sunil is currently sitting on 23 off 19 balls with a four and a six to his name, so it is certainly the start he wanted?"

"It's the start he needed Patty, and the start that India needed from him given what came before. They are currently well ahead of the rate, that's no problem, and well ahead of where England were at this stage. Sure they have lost one more wicket but I think they are ahead in the game. Trahar in particular has come out here ready to go and swinging. There has been a good battle between him and Hunter French, though Trahar is very much winning it at the moment. Hitting it cleanly and finding the gaps."

"What do you make of the England bowling performance so far?"

"I want to say it has been good – they have taken 3 wickets and sent

3 very dangerous batsmen back to the pavilion. But they have also been very expensive in doing so. Mo gave away 29 off 3 overs, Hunter 40 off 5, Jules 34 off 5, its too many. They have such a limited score to work with, they need to be tighter. Sonia is the only one who has impressed me so far this innings, 1-12 off her 3, keeping it below the required rate. She is having the same effect that Panda and Shubanka had earlier – the slow spin is putting pressure on the batsmen. Shame England don't have another spinner really."

"Can you call it from this point?"

"5 or 6 overs ago I would have said this game had moved slightly in England's favour. Now that these two are settled and scoring so quickly I have to give them the edge. We are only 16 overs in so far Patty! If you were batting first then by scoring 116 in the first 16 you would be targeting 350+, so 260 should be straightforward. But we are only 2 good balls or bad mistakes away from the tail, and then all bets are off. This game is on a knife edge and the next 10 overs will decide it. England will have to go more defensive to limit the scoring rate, but that means they will get less wicket opportunities. Would be good to hear Jones's thinking now! Anyway – I am going to try and see if I can get into the Levante box as one of Priyanka's entourage, they probably have all the high-end stuff in there! Andy will be taking my place here in the booth."

"Happy hunting Jon, and bring us back some jam scones if you find any. England are going to make a change in the bowling and Patrick Sherman is going to come on from the pavilion end. I guess Sonia will be switching back to her preferred Nursery End so that she can get the help down the slope? Sherman, the medium pacer, is just setting up a rather defensive field. 4 men out, fine leg, third man and 2 sweepers. The inside 5 are at point, short extra cover, mid-off, mid-on and square leg. There is no slip and no one anywhere close to the bat really. England have switched completely, and it is difficult to see where any big runs will come from. Lots of singles available though as apart from short extra cover all of the inside men are right on the 30-yard circle."

Sherman to **Sharma**, 1 run, wide and back of a length, driven down the ground slowly to **Jones** at mid-off.

Sherman to **Trahar**, 1 run, straighter, but too full and knocked back down the ground easily to **Jones** again. The captain has given away two easy singles.

Sherman to **Sharma**, no run, wide outside the off stump and left alone by the batsman, nipped back a bit off the seam but no trouble.

Sherman to **Sharma**, 1 run, drifting down the legside, back of a length, and clipped off the legs to **Khan** at fine leg.

Sherman to **Trahar**, no run, good ball, full and straight and defended by the batsman, who holds the position for 5 seconds after the ball.

Sherman to **Trahar**, 4 runs, tries the same delivery again, full and straight though the batsman is ready this time and drives it solidly back over the bowlers head and splits mid-on and mid-off exactly down the middle. After a couple of bounces it hits the white picket fence in front of the pavilion.

15:28 India 123-3 after 17 overs. England 96-2, RRR 4.18. "As expected Sonia has switched sides and will continue from the Nursery End. It still starts her second spell though, with her first spell figures of 3 overs, no maidens, 1 wicket for 12 runs. So far, the best of the English bowlers, but plenty of work still to do. Andy, welcome back, have you been impressed with Sonia so far?"

"It's too early to give a judgment. She has a wicket and a premium scalp so that's great, and she is keeping it much tighter than the rest of the bowling unit. So yes so far so good but I can't say impressive just yet. She needs to use her cricketing brain and work out how to put pressure on Sharma and Trahar now, get them back in the hut and give England a chance to win this game. She should know exactly how to get Sharma out given how much she has watched him over in India and should know his weaknesses."

"Well, Andy I can't see many, so hopefully she does have an inside track, can get inside his head and force him to make a mistake.

Trahar too has made a good start?"

"Yes he has, and in a very short period of time. 27 runs off 21 balls is fantastic one day cricket. Very much from a time gone by! They would have wanted him to be defensive and not risk anything after coming out to bat, and I don't think he really has taken many risks! Knocking the ball around into the gaps and when the bowlers make a mistake finding a gap to the boundary rope. He has solidly supported Sharma and together they have given India the upper hand in this game. The momentum is truly with them right now."

Chancellor to **Sharma**, no run, turn from the first ball of the new spell, pitches on middle and turns away into the keeper's gloves, past a watchful batsman.

Chancellor to **Sharma**, 1 run, little bit too full this time and with a big stride swept of the front foot past short leg and fielded by **Sherman** out at deep square leg.

Chancellor to **Trahar**, no run, arm? ball going straight on and defended out to short leg by the batsman.

Chancellor to **Trahar**, no run, flighted delivery on a full length defended again with the bat out in front of the pads. Exactly what the bowler would have hoped for, bringing the bat-pad and the short leg into play.

Chancellor to **Trahar**, 1 run, driven on the half volley down the ground to **French** at deep mid-on for a jogging single.

Chancellor to **Sharma**, no run, big spin on this one, pitching on middle and leg and turning past the batsman's edge, out through a 5th stump line. The batsman is a bit surprised and gives a knowing smirk back to the bowler, who is gasping with hands on her head.

15:32   India 125-3 after 18 overs. England 99-2, RRR: 4.25.

Sherman to **Trahar**, 6 runs, smashed! Short delivery is picked up very early by the batsman who gets square and pulls it hard off the middle of the bat up over backward square leg and into the Mound Stand at the bottom of the hill. Stand and deliver.

Sherman to **Trahar**, 2 runs, full delivery, half driven half cut away into the offside past the point fielder. **Jules** has to run around from 3rd man as it slows up before the ropes.

Sherman to **Trahar**, no run, quicker and flatter, left alone outside the off stump and through to the keeper.

Sherman to **Trahar**, 1 run, body line delivery, defended out into the leg side and **Chancellor** fields from mid-on.

Sherman to **Sharma**, no run, short and delivered into the ribs, defended and the bowler fields off his own bowling in the legside.

Sherman to **Sharma**, 2 runs, too full and driven into the offside past a diving short cover who gets a hand on the ball to stop a certain four. Fielded by **Hanson** sweeping around the boundary rope.

15:37   India 136-3 after 19 overs. England 107-2, RRR: 4.03.

Chancellor to **Trahar**, no run, she tries the googly first up, but it just stays straight and is defended out to short leg.

Chancellor to **Trahar**, 1 run, full ball driven down to **French** at deep mid-on.

Chancellor to **Sharma**, 2 runs, back of a length and drifting down the legside, clipped out through midwicket and fielded by **Sherman** running across the Grandstand to field at cow corner.

Chancellor to **Sharma**, no run, straighter ball defended back to the bowler, not much spin.

Chancellor to **Sharma**, 1 run, full ball, driven straight down the ground back to **French** at deep mid-on.

Chancellor to **Sharma**, 1 run, full but on the pads and swept on the volley after a big stride out, fielded by **Sherman** running in from the square leg boundary.

15:18 **toby @Tobytools:** @PPringles Who is this Levante woman?? Get her off the radio. Talk to people who actually know cricket!

15:19 **kiks @nikita_aol:** @PPringles OMG! @pinkyofficial is soooo amazing! Such a role model!

15:20 **Vikas @V4India:** *replying to @nikita_aol* Not only a role model .. pretty Hot too!! @CaptainSharma is a lucky guy!!

15:20 **toby @Tobytools:** @PPringles ok I just googled her! WOW yes please! … I'll allow it!

15:22 **kiks @nikita_aol:** @PPringles Ask her if she is engaged?!! That's what we want to know!

15:24 **Vikas @V4India:** @pinkyoffical is still free! I have a spare seat in the Grandstand if you want to join me!!

15:25 **Geoff @barmyGeoff:** @PPringles @SirJon @abirdman can we please just get back to the cricket now!?

15:26 **Craig @barmy1992:** *replying to @barmyGeoff* I don't mind, anything to distract from this bowling shambles. Trahar is smashing these boys all over the place.

15:29 **Vikas @V4India:** @PPringles @abirdman Trahar is outscoring @CaptainSharma here! He must be distracted by @pinkyofficial all over the radio.

15:30 **kiks @nikita_aol:** @PPringles @glassceiling100 is bowling fantastically. Showing the quickies how to keep the rate down. Still there is only one of her .. so see her through and then India can't lose!

15:33 **Vikas @V4India:** @PPringles BOOM!! Big maximum from the little guy! Used the pace on the ball and into the stands! Next time on this side please!

15:35 **Bobby @PigeonCricket:** @PPringles Oi Trahar! Stop aiming for us in the sky!! Can't a pigeon get some peace and quiet anymore?

15:36 **Bobby @PigeonCricket:** @PPringles @BCCELive has hit us before!! RIP to Bobby Snr now resting in the Lord's Museum.

15:37 **Craig @barmy1992:** @PPringles Only @glassceiling100 is keeping England in this game. Kudos to her.

15:38 **Geoff @barmyGeoff:** *replying to @barmy1992* Got to give the Indian captain some credit. He is solid with the bat and very hard to bowl at! Doesn't give anything away.

15:39 **kiks @nikita_aol:** *replying to @barmyGeoff* There's a reason why he's the best batsman in the world, and our Indian hero today!

15:40 India 141-3 after 20 overs. England 117-2, RRR 4.00.

Sherman to **Trahar**, no run, outside off stump, swung at but missed! Little smile of success from the bowler.

Sherman to **Trahar**, 4 runs, smile doesn't last long, too full and lofted with a straight drive over the umpire and quickly rolls into the pavilion fencing.

Sherman to **Trahar**, 2 runs, back of a length and cut strongly outside the off stump. A diving point gets a hand to it but can only slow it down for **Jules** to field around from 3rd man.

Sherman to **Trahar**, 1 run, straighter delivery on the pads and defended slowly out to **Chancellor** at mid-on but the batsman take her arm on and get through for an easy single.

Sherman to **Sharma**, 1 run, clipped off the pads down to **Khan** at fine leg.

Sherman to **Trahar**, 2 runs, driven full past short extra cover and up the hill to the Grandstand. Has to be fielded on the dive by **Hanson** who is sweeping that boundary. Very expensive over from England at just the wrong time.

15:44 India 151-3 after 21 overs. England 122-3, RRR 3.79. "England continue with Chancellor from the Nursery End; it seems like they have little choice at the moment except to bowl her through and try and rotate at the other end. She is the only bowler able to contain the run rate, although she hasn't looked threatening to either of these two in a while. Sharma happy to knock the ball around while Trahar does all the heavy lifting, he has moved quickly onto 48 now!"

Chancellor to **Sharma**, no run, flighted delivery drifting off the pads, and spinning. Defended by the batsman.

Chancellor to **Sharma**, 1 run, driven on the front foot down the ground to **Khan.**

Chancellor to **Trahar**, 2 runs, full delivery though not much spin and clipped off the pads out into the legside, they risk a second on the throw of **Sherman**, who is usually very accurate, though he feels the pressure and sends it to the wrong end. That's the 50 up for Trahar, and a very impressive 50 at that. He raises his bat to a massive ovation from the Indian fans and gets a hug from his captain. The noise in the stadium is boisterous.

Chancellor to **Trahar**, no run, good delivery to sharpen the batsman after the milestone. Turning away past the bat and into the gloves.

Chancellor to **Trahar**, 1 run, driven down the ground to **French** at deep mid-on.

Chancellor to **Sharma**, 1 run, swept very fine off a straight line and the non-striker calls through for a very quick single before **Barnes** can get around to field.

15:48   India 156-3 after 22 overs. England 131-2, RRR 3.75. "Andy, step in here, England need to do something different no?"

"Firstly let me say this has been a great recovery from India led by Trahar with a great half-century, and still going. He hasn't shown any respect to some very average bowling and scored very quickly. Most of his big shots will be part of tonight's highlight reel and he is fully deserving of the ovation from this pretty loud and partisan crowd. On the other side England have been very woeful. They just haven't got anything out of these conditions, which should suit them very well. There is a bit of a breeze, it's not too hot, the ball has the opportunity to move around though they just can't get anything working. Khan, French and Sherman have been very poor this afternoon, no control and they have deserved to be hit around the park. Yes, England need to do something different now just to create something. They need wickets, that's the only thing that is going to get them through this game. It's all ok if Sonia is not conceding runs, but even she has an economy rate higher than the run rate required. She is also quickly running out of overs. If they don't take some wickets and get into the tail then this game is going to end very quickly."

"Well it looks like England are going to give Sherman one more chance and let's see what happens. However, they are starting to roll the dice now and they have put in a slip, taking out the square leg, and short cover has gone under the hat at short leg. They are trying to force a breakthrough here."

Sherman to **Sharma**, 2 runs, thick edge of a wide delivery and it goes down through the gully region. Point can't quite get there with the dive and it is left to **Jules** from 3rd man to clean up and they get back for 2.

Sherman to **Sharma**, 1 run, on middle stump and bouncing, though slow enough to get a pull away into the leg side. **French** fields on the midwicket boundary as they jog through for one.

Sherman to **Trahar**, 2 runs, too full, trying to bring the slip into play and driven through the covers. There is protection on the boundary though it's quite straight and **Hanson** has to cover a lot of ground to collect and get it into the bowler's end.

Sherman to **Trahar**, no run, aggressive ball, short and into the chest, defended up on his toes down to **King** at short leg.

Sherman to **Trahar**, 1 run, short ball again and punched out to the leg side, **French** runs quickly from the boundary to stop a second run.

Sherman to **Sharma**, no run, up into the ribs again of a short ball, quick too. The batsman is able to fend it off just to the right of short leg, who recovers quickly to stop a single.

15:53   India 162-3 after 23 overs. England 135-4, RRR: 3.67.

Chancellor to **Trahar**, wide, off target from the bowler as she tries to get one to turn from outside the leg stump but it goes straight on and down the legside. Keeper makes a good adjustment to get there but the **Umpire Randall** has no problem in calling that one and stretching out his arms.

Chancellor to **Trahar**, no run, straighter line and a bit of turn, defended back down to the bowler.

Chancellor to **Trahar**, no run, lots of spin on this one as it turns away from the bat on a great line though doesn't get the edge and it goes into the gloves.

Chancellor to **Trahar**, no run, flighted delivery staying straight, and the batsman takes no risk by defending it out to **King** at short leg.

Chancellor to **Trahar**, 2 runs, ah the pressure is off and a straight ball gets driven off the legs out to midwicket. There are no fielders in the circle and so they get 2 while **Sherman** runs around from deep square leg to field.

Chancellor to **Trahar**, no run, the googly, pitching on off stump and turning slightly to middle, not much turn and watched carefully by the batsman onto the bat.

Chancellor to **Trahar**, no run, good end to a very tight over, spinning on off stump and left alone by the batsman as it spins out toward the slip, but taken neatly by the keeper.

15:56   India 165-3 after 24 overs. England 141-4, RRR: 3.69. "That was a fantastic over from Sonia and apart from that one loose delivery she had Trahar shut up. Lots of variation of length, speed and spin. She has started a good battle here against Trahar though it may be a little bit too late? In any case England are going to make a change now from the pavilion end. They need to start taking some wickets to stay in this game and captain Jones is turning to old Mr Reliable in Mark Jules. He has had so much success here over the years and England really need him to get them back into this game. They will go with a tight field, a slip, 3rd man, point, extra cover, mid-off, mid-on, deep midwicket, short leg and finally fine leg. I am expecting some swinging stuff and some short stuff, he is going to have to mix it up to make a breakthrough between these two."

Jules to **Sharma**, 6 runs, it's a terrible start to his new spell, with a loose delivery, thrown down short and not much pace, picked off easily by a well-set batsman and pulled up and over the deep man at square leg and into the stands.

Jules to **Sharma**, no run, much better line and length and respected by the batsman and left alone.

Jules to **Sharma**, 1 run, short though not enough and it can be batted down into the legside without much trouble and must be fielded by **King** running back from short leg.

Jules to **Trahar**, wide, it's short again and this time down the leg side, and easy decision for the **Umpire du Toit**. Jules is furious with himself and screams out in anger which scares a bunch of the pigeons which are feeding on the square just to the right of the wicket. The pigeons fly up and the batsman and the bowler have to duck to avoid getting hit. No damage done and the pigeons go back to their afternoon tea, out of the way of the action. *Remember to follow all our pigeon action live across social media @PigeonCricket.*

Jules to **Trahar**, 1 run, full and on off stump and driven out into the covers for the sweeper **Hanson** to field.

Jules to **Sharma**, 2 runs, full delivery to finish the over and picked up early by the settled batsman and driven back straight down the ground towards the pavilion. **Chancellor** and **French** both chase after it and work together to stop the boundary and get the ball back to the bowler's wicket. **Umpire du Toit** has called 'over' there, but by my count there should be another ball? There have been too many mistakes from these umpires today. Anyway, that was definitely not the over that England wanted for Jules' return. They are under serious pressure now, not that the pigeons care about that.

CHAPTER 9
ENGLAND 260 ALL OUT, INDIA 176-3.

16:00 "India 176-3 after 25 overs. England 150-4, RRR: 3.4. It is now 4 o'clock in the afternoon and we will step away from the cricket for a few minutes and hand back to the main studio to bring you the 4pm scheduled shipping forecast. For our overseas listeners this is a broadcast of the weather conditions around the United Kingdom for the maritime industry out at sea."

"The shipping forecast, issued by the Met office on behalf of the Maritime and Coastguard Agency at 1, 6, double O, today, the 19th of June. The general synopsis at 1, 8, double O, stable, occasional rain, Northern Hebrides, 995, South 5-7. West of Shannon, showers, 1000, west gales 8. Now the shipping forecast for the next 24h around the United Kingdom.

Viking, south, 5, occasional rain, moderate becoming good.

North Ultshire, South Ultshire, southwest, 4, occasional rain, good.

Forties, south veering southwest, 4, showers, moderate becoming poor.

Cromarty, Forth, southwest, 3, occasional rain, moderate.

Tyne, Doggar, south, 5, rain, moderate becoming good.

Fisher, southwest, 4, poor becoming moderate.

German Bight, south, 5, occasional rain, good becoming moderate.

Humber, south veering southwest, 4, rain, moderate.

Thames, south, 3, good.

Dover, wight, south, 3, moderate becoming good.

Portland, southwest veering west, 4, good.

Plymouth, southwest veering west, 5, moderate becoming good.

Biscay, west, 4, good."

16:02   **toby @Tobytools:** @PPringles @abirdman what is this?? What happened to the cricket?

16:02   **Jon Knight @SirJon:** *replying to @Tobytools* are you even English? How do you not know what the Shipping Forecast is?

16:03   **Andy @abirdman:** *replying to* @Tobytools we have no choice but to switch to the forecast. It has to be at the same time every day. Has been like that for 100 years!

16:03   **Geoff @barmyGeoff:** @PPringles And the crowd go wild!! Let's get back in the game!! Its about time.

16:03   **toby @Tobytools:** *replying to @barmyGeoff* what happened??

16:04   **Vikas @V4India:** @PPringles we are still way ahead in this game!! No worries! Credit where it is due, looked like a ripper of ball from here.

16:04   **Craig @barmy1992:** *replying to @barmyGeoff* I would have been pissed if he dropped that!

16:04   **Geoff @barmyGeoff:** @PPringles full credit to @glassceiling100. Controlled the run-rate, put pressure on .. forced the mistake!

16:05   **toby @Tobytools:** @PPringles AHHH!! Screw the sailors. Why are they sailing in this rain anyway. Get back to the action!

16:05   **kiks @nikita_aol:** @PPringles How long is this going to go on?? We are missing all the action because the British need their "fish and chips"!

16:06   **Vikas @V4India:** @PPringles well batted sir! Got us back in this game, can't lose it from here!! Leave it to @greatwhitepanda to finish it off!

16:06   **kiks @nikita_aol:** *replying to @V4India* Who is out??? Isn't Singh coming in before Panda?? Did they switch the order?? Can someone please tell us what is going on??

"Trafalgar, west, 4, moderate becoming good.

Fitzroy, Sole, west, 5, good becoming moderate.

Lundy, southwest veering to west, 4, occasional showers, good becoming moderate.

Fastnet, west, 5, occasional shower, good.

Irish sea, southwest veering to west, 4, occasional showers, good becoming moderate.

Shannon, Rockwell, west, gales 8, regular showers, moderate becoming poor.

Malin, south, 6 becoming 7, occasional showers, moderate.

Hebrides, south, 7 becoming gales 8, occasional showers, poor.

Bailey, southwest veering west, gales 8, moderate becoming poor.

Fair Isle, south, 5, occasional rain, moderate becoming poor.

Faeroes, south, 6 becoming 7, occasional showers, moderate.

Southeast Iceland, south, 6, occasional showers, moderate becoming good."

16:08   **Vikas   @V4India:**   @PPringles   great   over   from @glassceiling100 given the situation. Fair play to her.

16:09   **Geoff @barmyGeoff:** @PPringles go on Jules! Put some pressure on the new boy! Get some bouncers up at his head.

16:10   **Jon Knight @SirJon:** @PPringles That is the 50 up for @CaptainSharma! Well batted, a captain's innings.

16:10   **Vikas @V4India:** @PPringles @abirdman What a time to bring up his 50! Like the postman – he always delivers for India.

16:10   **Craig @barmy1992:** *replying to @barmyGeoff* Forget bouncers, the ball is moving all over the place from where I am sitting! Get it full and moving.

16:11 **Vikas @V4India:** @PPringles oh dear god!

16:11 **Craig @barmy1992:** *replying to @barmyGeoff* Have all the Indian fans left?? Ole Ole Ole Ole!! What a delivery! Corker!

16:12 **Geoff @barmyGeoff:** *replying to @barmy1992* you called it mate, full and swinging and the stumps go everywhere!

16:12 "India 184-5 after 27 overs. England 170-4, RRR: 3.35. Welcome back to Lord's and just in time too as it is all change here, with India now 185 for 5 having lost both established batsmen in back-to-back overs. That's how fast it can change in cricket! India looked set to quickly finish off this game but with two new batsmen at the crease and England getting into the tailenders this game is wide open again. England need 5 wickets, India need only 77 runs, and we have plenty of overs left. Andy what do you make of it all?"

"What a terrible time to go away for the shipping forecast. As much love as I have for those sailors and their safety, this game has completely turned on its head now, and I can't believe our fans missed it. Let's look back at the Sonia over first, so efficient, gave nothing away for the first 3 balls, tight lines and length. Got a bit looser with that fourth delivery, was too short and was there to be hit – but Trahar gets it all wrong, attempts the slog sweep, hits it high on the bat and it goes straight up into the air. It seemed to me to be in the air for ages, but French made very good ground, running across from deep mid-on to take the catch."

"At this level you don't expect him to drop that, but I agree with you it was all about the pressure that Sonia was putting on Trahar. It started the previous over and it was almost out of frustration that he tried to heave that away. And then what can you say about Jules?"

"This was the crucial wicket that England needed. Sharma would have been singled out as the dangerman before the start of play and he proved so with a very stable and competent 50. Fantastic ball from Jules, inswing, full, you miss then I hit cricket. Love to see it, and it has wrestled England right back into this game."

16:04

| S K Trahar | c. French | 57 off 55 balls | FOW: 176-4 |
| | b. Chancellor | | |

16:10

| Sunil Sharma | b. Jules | 52 off 46 balls | FOW: 184-5 |

"We now have 2 new batsmen at the crease – Nikil Panda and A P Singh the wicketkeeper. Both can swing the bat and have the quality to get India over the line here, but were you surprised with the decision to promote Panda?"

"Surprised, but not shocked. India are in such a commanding position that they would have wanted to finish the game off quickly. Remember big wins like this can set up the entire series – this is not just a one-game affair. Panda's big hitting can demoralise any bowling team and the coach would have been thinking let's turn the screws here and get a psychological advantage into Friday's game. If Sharma had been up in the dressing room, rather than in the middle I don't think he would have made the same call though. He would have known this game was not yet over and would have appreciated the sensible style of Singh. But such is life and it doesn't really matter now, as they are both out there anyway. Would be good to hear Sharma's thoughts on it if Mike can get in to see him! In the meantime, let's get back to the action!"

Chancellor to **Panda**, 2 runs, pulled away into the legside off a short ball and **Sherman** runs around from square to get it before the boundary.

Chancellor to **Panda**, no run, back of a length and left alone outside spinning outside the off stump.

Chancellor to **Panda**, **caught**, flighted delivery with some spin out the back of the hand, the batsman goes for a big drive over the covers but can't quite get to the pitch of it and it takes an sharp thick edge.

Jones is there at slip, diving to his right and takes it one handed a foot off the ground.

16:14

| Nikil Panda | ct. Jones | 4 off 6 balls | FOW: 186-6 |
| | b. Chancellor | | |

"This is very quickly turning into a collapse Andy! Chancellor gets her third and has led England's fight back into this game. 260 is now looking further and further away!"

"Patty, it was a crazy shot to try and attempt and he will be very annoyed at himself. Chancellor, the only bowler who has shown India any trouble only has 9 balls left, see them out and then fill your boots when the quicks come back on. They have been bowling terribly! That should have been their strategy and Panda knows it. We can't deny that Sonia is having a great game though! Hardly given any runs away and has got her wicket too. England are into the tail now certainly and may very well just turn this game around. What a rollercoaster ride."

"While we have a couple of minutes waiting for Shubanka, who was probably relaxing with a cup of tea 5 minutes ago and wasn't even thinking about batting, let's go across to Ray who can tell us about the Trahar and Sharma innings."

"Thanks Patty, and wow has this game got my head spinning. Trahar and Sharma both played exceptionally well. They took the game to England and made England's world class attack look very village. Trahar first – 57 off 55 balls, lots of shots for the highlights program: 5 fours and a big 6 off Sherman. Runs came mainly through midwicket, almost 40%, with the next best area straight down the ground. Normally he is quite cute with his cutting and pulling, though apart from the big hit, which arguably was over square leg, there was very little behind the stumps, only 13 including that 6. He treated Sherman with a lot of disdain, taking 26 off the 15 balls he faced against him. By comparison he faced 27 balls off Chancellor, including the wicket ball, and only got 16 runs. She managed to lock him down, and the frustration forced the mistake. Secondly the Captain, Sharma, 52 off 46 balls, innings seemed almost pedestrian when compared with the big-hitting Trahar, though he actually accumulated more quickly. 2 sixes, including the "welcome back" for Jules, and a four, in an otherwise riskless innings. He likes to bat in front of the wicket as we know and showed that today. 21 runs down the ground, 16 through midwicket and 6 in the covers. He faced a lot of deliveries from Chancellor, 3 full overs in fact, and managed to navigate her well, unlike his colleagues. Took it slowly and got 13 off her, but then milked the quicker bowlers – 18 off French and 13 of Jules. Finally what did they do together? They had a 4th wicket partnership of 99 off 89 balls which changed this game in India's favour. I'm sure they would have liked to bring up the century partnership, and my guess is India would have romped home if they had stayed out there. If India win it will be because this partnership gave them another chance. An Indian victory looked all but certain a few overs ago, now none of us are that sure."

Chancellor to **Shubanka**, no run, flighted delivery on middle and defended away to short leg.

Chancellor to **Shubanka**, no run, testing delivery outside the off stump but left alone watchfully.

Chancellor to **Shubanka**, 1 run, full ball driven back down the ground to **French**.

16:20   India 187-6 after 28 overs. England 181-4, RRR: 3.36. "We are going to bring Bobby Jungan back into the booth alongside you Andy, just as we are getting to the final stages of this game. Bobby what do you make of the last 20 mins and which way is this game going?"

"This is why I love cricket, Patty. There was one-way traffic, it looks like the game is signed and sealed for India, then everything changes. I think Andy used the word 'rollercoaster' a few minutes ago and maybe that sums up whole match today, but the last 20 minutes have been freefall for India. Trahar lost his composure under the pressure then Panda played a crazy shot given the situation. Certainly Panda will feel like he has let the side down, especially after coming in up the order. Unluckily in the middle of those two, Sharma got an unplayable delivery. Inswinging, full and fast, very impressive from a hall of fame bowler. We are now into the tail now and unless Singh can step up, control the strike and be there at the end, this game could be over very quickly. We have plenty of time left, take it easy, don't do anything stupid and this will be a coast to the finish. I just hope we have the mental game to do that."

"Chancellor, the main pick the of the English bowlers today has only got one over left and then England are going to have to go back to their quick men. Now that the big middle order partnership is behind us, this could be the perfect time to do just that. Can you pick a winner Bobby?"

"It is very difficult, very balanced. All the momentum is currently with England, new batsmen at the crease, into the tail. Though India only need 70 odd runs and still have 20 overs to get there. Right now I would pick India to maintain their composure and get the job done. But I wouldn't bet on it. Andy?"

"Well I'll take the other side then just to be fair. I think England have the bit between their teeth, they are moving around the field with more energy, chirping away, excited. They sense an opportunity here that seemed impossible only 20 mins ago. I think they will take the wickets they need to close out this game. If they don't though, as Bobby says, it's a straightforward chase."

Jules to **Shubanka**, no run, fast and back of a length, rising and left alone by the batsman.

Jules to **Shubanka**, 1 run, just straightening and clipped off the pads down to fine leg. Not much technique there but got it away and down to **Khan.**

Jules to **Singh**, 1 run, he's been out there a while though this is his first ball, and it's too full, driven easily out into the covers for the sweeper **Hanson.**

Jules to **Shubanka**, no run, short and spicy, up into the rib cage of the batsman who fends it off on his tip toes, just avoiding spooning it to short leg.

Jules to **Shubanka**, 1 run, tries the short ball again though it's a bit too full and can be clipped easily down to **Khan** again.

Jules to **Singh**, 2 runs, pitched up and swinging though it is shown a full face of the bat and the speed of the ball carries it straight past the bowler and down the ground. **Hanson** is able to chase after it and gets a nice round of applause from the members now enjoying the day in the pavilion.

16:24   India 192-6 after 29 overs. England 187-4, RRR: 3.29.

Chancellor to **Shubanka**, wide, flights it but loses some control and it pitches outside leg stump and is left alone by the batsman, who doesn't expect any turn. **Umpire Randall** raises his arms and signals a wide.

Chancellor to **Shubanka**, no run, nice line and length, arm delivery going straight on, picked by the leg spinner batsman and defended.

Chancellor to **Shubanka**, 1 run, too full on the leg stump and punched on the half volley out into the legside where **Sherman** has to do quick work to avoid a second run.

Chancellor to **Singh**, **caught**, what a catch! Flighted delivery deceives the batsman who is not sure whether to play forward or back, and half paddles it out into the legside. **King** is quick with his movements, sticks out his left hand into the air and the ball sticks! Quick reactions and great catch, his second of the day in that position and a fourth for Chancellor.

| A P Singh | ct. King | 3 off 3 balls | FOW: 194-7 |
| | b. Chancellor | | |

"Andy, what a catch that was, he is becoming a specialist in that position?"

"It certainly seems like that from the two catches that he has taken, and catches win matches! England are having a big party in the middle at the moment. The last recognised batsman is out, 3 wickets away from what I thought would be a very unlikely victory. Sam is new to the team and moments like that can change a career. He could have been looking at "one and done" given the strength England have in reserve, though by taking those catches, potentially getting a victory here, England may go with the same winning team next time and then you have more chances to impress and become a regular on the team sheet. Although he will not want to be at short leg his whole career if he can avoid it!"

"England are very much into the tail now and for the last few balls of Chancellor's over it looks like the whole field is coming up. She has taken four key wickets already and the whole team are trying to get her a 5-for. Getting on the honours boards would be a fair reward for her potentially match-winning shift today. Mopal is the new batsman and he is faced with a slip, leg slip, short leg and silly point."

Chancellor to **Mopal**, 2 runs, driven off the pads out past short leg and into the midwicket area. **Sherman** is too square to cut off the second run as he comes around to sweep the boundary.

Chancellor to **Mopal**, no run, flighted outside the off stump with some spin and left alone by the batsman.

Chancellor to **Mopal**, 2 runs, driven off a full pitched delivery off the meat of the bat and out into the offside where there is only protection on the boundary, by **Hanson**.

16:30 India 198-7 after 30 overs. England 193-5, RRR: 3.15. "That's the end of a great spell from Chancellor, she has really changed this game for England and put them in a winning position. Ray can you give us her stats whilst she gets some congratulations from all her teammates?"

"It has been a fantastic day for her and a shame she didn't make the boards. The spinners have had all the rub of this wicket all day today. In this spell specifically she was a real trooper and bowled 7 overs on the trot. Not that Jones could afford to take her off. 7 overs, no maidens, 3 wickets for 27 runs. That gives her figures for the day of 10 overs, no maidens, 4 wickets for 39 runs, a real masterclass of spin bowling in unsuited conditions. From her pitch map we can see 42% of balls outside the off stump and 45% on middle. That is a very tight line. 60% of her deliveries were on a good length or just back of a length, with only 5 short balls, one of which got Trahar out!. Her captain and country will be very proud of her, especially if they can now go on to finish the job."

"Thanks Ray. Jules to continue from the pavilion end. England are going to come in with an aggressive field now to take these last few wickets. They have put in an extra slip and brought in a short cover. They now only have protection on the boundaries at fine leg and deep midwicket."

Jules to **Shubanka**, no run, wide outside the off stump and left alone, without risk.

Jules to **Shubanka**, no run, straighter ball, still back of a length and rising, defended out into the legside.

Jules to **Shubanka**, 1 run, slapped at it with a cross bat outside the off stump and can only get an edge of sorts out into the covers, but they can scamper through for a single before **Rhodes** fetches it from point.

Jules to **Mopal**, 2 runs, lovely shot off a full ball, just leans on a cover drive and pushes it past the short cover out towards the Grandstand. **French** has to back up from mid-off to stop a third run. That brings up the 200 for India and the batsmen bump fists in the middle. 60 runs to go in the chase and plenty of time still to do it.

Jules to **Mopal**, 1 run, straight ball but not very fast and defended into the vacant midwicket area. **King** runs back from short leg to field.

Jules to **Shubanka**, no run, short and ducked under by the batsman, who asks for a wide signal but doesn't get it this time.

16:35   India 202-7 after 31 overs. England 201-5, RRR: 3.11. "So, Sonia has finished all her overs, Jules has a few left, but I guess England are in a bit of a bind now. Who do they turn to Andy?"

"Khan, French and Sherman have been pretty poor today, though it seems like they last bowled hours ago. We have a new set of batsmen at the crease and favourable circumstances for any bowling unit. Who doesn't like bowling at tailenders? They should all be shouting at Jones to give them the ball next."

"Ok Jones has thrown the ball across to Mo Khan to replace Chancellor from the nursery end. A big call. He last bowled almost 2 hours ago and has been idling in the long grass out of the way for most of this innings. England set him an aggressive field to try and keep the pressure on."

Khan to **Mopal**, wide, first ball is very loose outside the off stump. Outside of the guidelines for the umpire and after a second of thought **Umpire Randall** signals wide. Now remember, umpire, to add on an extra ball!

Khan to **Mopal**, no run, better angle of attack, in towards the batsman who defends it solidly back to the bowler.

Khan to **Mopal, review,** complete commotion exploding in the middle of the pitch right now. The ball was fine, on the stumps and defended out into the legside. **King** from short leg turns to chase it down while the batsman starts a run, but then the striker sends the non-striker back! After a quick turn **King** tries to throw down the stumps at the bowlers end but the non-striking batsman deflects it with his outstretched bat. **Umpire Randall,** not convinced it was an accident, has given him out! After a lot of screaming and hand gesturing, he has and asked for a review from the third umpire. The soft signal is out.

"Third umpire to TV director, we have an umpire review. The call on the field is out for Obstructing the Field. I need to see the angle of the throw and if any deliberate movement was made by the batsman. Firstly can we have the view from behind the fielder. Ok. The angle is ok, but not convincing that it would have hit the stumps. Can I please see the batsman now? Ok here he stops, turns around. Ok there is no ball yet. Please roll it forward, forward, ok there is the ball, there it hits the bat. Ok can you zoom out on that please. He attempts to dive for the line, he moves towards the ball there. Please rock and roll that. Ok, I have made my decision. Umpire Randall, there is not enough information on the tv view to overturn your on-field decision. Please keep with your on-field decision – out."

16:38

Shubanka	Obstructing the field	5 off 14 balls	FOW: 203-8

"Bobby there is uproar in the stands and on the field. The batsman has to go but there is shouting from the Indian dressing room at the umpire. What is going on here?"

"I have never seen that live before Patty, really rare. But the rules are the rules. The batsman is not allowed to intentionally interfere with the direction of the ball after it goes into the field. Ok this happens all the time by accident, and "by design by accident" if you know what I mean. The batsman is always trying to protect his wicket by cutting out the throw to the stumps. But if it hits him it's an accident. If it hits him and goes for more runs, say the boundary, then it just counts as overthrows! Just ask Ben Stokes from the World Cup Final 11 years ago! Here the umpire must have seen something which suggested that the batsman was watching the fielder and moved his bat in a way to try and hit the ball. Apart from their ball counting the umpires have been pretty good today so if Randall saw something then he has to act on it. The intent in real time can't be captured on the TV cameras, so we have to trust him. Very disappointing for India, but honestly their problems started 40 mins ago. They have lost their focus and maybe this match. Two of these guys now need to hunker down and just bat for as long as possible. Even if they score no runs, they will get time in the middle and start to work out these conditions which will be very useful for the rest of the series."

"Andy how do we account for that wicket?"

"Don't ask me. I don't think it counts to anyone. The bowler certainly not as it is more like a run out. But I don't think the fielder either as he didn't actually hit the stumps. So I guess it becomes like a retired hurt? You just leave and head off to the showers. It's been a very strange day on that front. King hit his own wicket this morning for a golden duck remember! For this one, Shubanka must have moved towards the ball or the umpire would have just ignored it. Strange, but 'out' is called, and in this sport you don't get to argue with the umpires. I'm sure he will go and double check rule 37 in the book when he gets back to the pavilion."

"Crazy, but he has accepted it, and now Deepak Pooran is coming in for India. In cricket you just don't argue with the umpires! They are 8 down and need a real miracle here to get a win."

Khan to **Mopal**, no run, wide and rising, left alone outside the off stump.

Khan to **Mopal**, 2 runs, short and on leg stump, deserved to be hit to the boundary, but get a bit higher than he expected and it can only be slapped into the legside. **Barnes** runs around from deep midwicket and can't stop a quick second.

Khan to **Mopal**, no run, much better length, in the block-hole, respected by the batsman and defended.

Khan to **Mopal**, 2 runs, wide again and swings at this one. Gets the edge that the bowler was looking for, but it is wide of second slip, almost down through the gully region. It's a thick edge but a long slow outfield for **Hanson** to chase into. The bowler won't necessarily be angry with that, the ball was hit uppish and next time perhaps to a fielder.

16:30 **Geoff @barmyGeoff:** @PPringles I agree with you! Fantastic spell from @glassceiling100, turned the game around for us!

16:31 **Craig @barmy1992:** *replying to @barmyGeoff* give that girl a big glass of red! She deserves a sit down! Well done!

16:33 **toby @Tobytools:** @PPringles I could do @dizzydora's job any day of the week! Just reads out some figures and give some poor chat. Here's one for you mate .. what is the correlation between you talking and people going to sleep!?

16:35 **kiks @nikita_aol:** *replying to @Tobytools* It's better listening to him than the shipping forecast again and missing the whole game!

16:37 **Vikas @V4India:** @PPringles what is going on out there? He can't be out! That was an accident.

16:38 **Craig @barmy1992:** *replying to @V4India* Agree mate, harsh luck, looked accidental from back here.

16:38 **toby @Tobytools:** @Jungan_Official and his Pakis are cheaters!! Whole thing is fixed. Pack them all off back to where they came from.

16:39 **Vikas @V4India:** @PPringles This is crazy! India make some noise! We can't stand for this!

16:40 **kiks @nikita_aol:** @PPringles what is this law 37?? Obviously, it was a mistake. Look at the replay there is nothing there! Umpires are so biased!

16:41 **Jon Knight @SirJon:** @PPringles This is going down to the wire! Run rate only 3 an over but only 2 wickets in hand!

16:38 **Twitter:** @Tobytools This tweet has been blocked for containing false and misleading information. It is now under review in line with our terms and conditions.

16:41 India 207-8 after 32 overs. England 205-6, RRR: 3.00. "Jules is going to take a break after a 4 over spell from the pavilion end and will be replaced by Hunter French. England are still going with an aggressive field, they need the wickets, time won't save them. 2 slips, short leg, short cover, deep protection on the cover and midwicket boundary, and at fine leg."

French to **Pooran**, 1 run, not a convincing first shot, Chinese cut away past the stumps down to **Jules** at fine leg.

French to **Mopal**, no run, full and straight, stamped out at the batsman's feet.

French to **Mopal**, no run, good variation, back of a length and swinging away from the batsman, perhaps with some reverse swing late in the evening?

French to **Mopal**, 1 run, driven on the front foot out into the covers to the sweeper **Sherman** marshalling the fence.

French to **Pooran**, no run, short and aggressive into the batsman's neck. Batsman is tall enough though to jump on top of it and defend it down on the legside. Exactly the kind of delivery that excites short leg and brings him into the game.

French to **Pooran**, 2 runs, too full and easily driven back down the ground towards the pavilion. Straight fielders are too wide and **Chancellor** finally fields before they think about a third run. A good over lost on the last ball.

16:45 India 211-8 after 33 overs. England 210-6, RRR: 2.94.

Khan to **Mopal**, no run, fast ball, quick and straight, defended back down the pitch.

Khan to **Mopal**, no run, short stuff now, banged in and rising to head height. Batsman watches it carefully and sways away to the offside just in time.

Khan to **Mopal**, 2 runs, driven off a length ball into the covers, there is no protection for **Khan** on the cover boundary, but **French** helps him out by getting there in time and getting the ball back in.

Khan to **Mopal**, 1 run, fended off down the legside and it trickles down to **Jules** at fine leg.

Khan to **Pooran**, no run, inswinging yorker, right at his feet, brilliant ball which has all the fielders gasping with their hands on their heads.

Defended by the batsman while almost falling over.

Khan to **Pooran**, 1 run, releases the pressure with a short ball on middle which can be turned into the leg side easily for **Barnes** on the boundary to run in for.

16:50 India 215-8 after 34 overs. England 221-6, RRR: 2.88. "Surprisingly Andy, just looking at the trackers and England were ahead at this point! I guess not that surprising given the flurry of wickets that England lost at the end of their innings to end it so early. It seems like this pitch hasn't been as flat as we thought it would be?"

"Certainly a tough pitch, but the shot selection hasn't been that great either. Both sides will go away knowing they have thrown wickets away today and no doubt get a rollicking from their coaches. I was really pleased with Hunter's first over back. He had been knocked all over by Sharma and Trahar earlier and has come back fresher and more consistent. Mo Khan is just having an off day today. Needs to put his legs up have a breather and come back fresh again on Friday. We know he is world class and hopefully he shows it throughout the rest of the series."

French to **Pooran**, no run, back of a length and left alone.

French to **Pooran**, 1 run, clipped off the pads down to **Jules** at fine leg, and a jogged through single.

French to **Mopal**, no run, short and defended back down the ground and fielded by the bowler himself.

French to **Mopal, caught,** edged and taken. Quicker delivery and full, the batsman attempts a full drive but can't get to the pitch of it and takes a big edge out to second slip. **Hanson** takes it comfortably at chest height right under his nose.

16:53

| Varun Mopal | ct. Hanson b. French | 15 off 19 balls | FOW: 216-9. |

"The end is nigh for India now. They still need another 45 runs and only have one wicket left in hand. That leaves number 10 and 11 at the crease for a last hoorah. Can they make a 10th wicket stand here? Pooran has an extended chat with Azer Khan, the new batsman, taking all the time he needs to settle him down. England are taking no prisoners here and have to go in for the kill. Men everywhere around the bat, they want this last wicket badly."

French to **Khan**, no run, outside off stump and left by the batsman.

French to **Khan**, 1 run, he gets some bat on it and drives it out into the offside. **Sherman** is patrolling that boundary and restricts it to only one.

16:56   India 217-9 after 35 overs. England 226-7, RRR: 2.93.

Khan to **Khan**, no run, back of a length, and left alone on length, mature batting as it sails over the stumps.

Khan to **Khan**, 1 run, drifting out onto the pads and easy enough to clip away down to fine leg even for a lower order batsman. Fielded by **Jules** running in from the ropes.

Khan to **Pooran**, 1 run, full delivery, driven solidly down the ground, but these two aren't that quick between the wickets and **Chancellor** limits the damage to only 1 run.

Khan to **Khan**, no run, short delivery, banged in and ducked under by the batsman. There is a look across to the legside umpire for a no ball or wide but no joy.

Khan to **Khan**, wide, this time he gets the umpire's attention, too short and too high, sails over the standing batsman, and an easy wide call for **Umpire Randall**.

Khan to **Khan**, no run, full swinging ball, but it swings away and misses everything as the batsman attempts a drive. A swing and miss will energise the bowler.

Khan to **Khan**, 1 run, half volley length and gets the treatment out through the open cover, but the boundary is well covered by **Sherman**. That shot deserved more than just one.

"And that will be drinks. 14 overs to go, India need another 40 runs but only have one wicket left. England have turned this game around completely in the last hour. At 176-3 with two batsmen on or nearing 50s England were looking down the barrel of the gun. 20 mins later and the tables were turned. The Indian Captain, Sunil Sharma, has taken this drinks opportunity to come and talk to his last batsmen. What do you think he is telling them Bobby?"

"What can you say in this situation? Keep your heads down, try and get through as many overs as we can. Don't take any risks – there is no need with a run rate required of less than 3 an over. Although it would have probably been useful to give half his team that same advice. They have thrown away a winning position in this match and that will hurt even more than losing it. Win predictor is now 95% in England's favour, but that still gives India a 5% chance of getting over the line. So maybe the fat lady hasn't started singing just yet?"

CHAPTER 10
ENGLAND 260 ALL OUT. INDIA 221-9.

17:00   "India 221-9 after 36 overs. England 230-7, RRR: 2.86.

"It will be Hunter French to continue and England continue being very aggressive. The keeper, Quince, has come up to the stumps, there are 2 slips back 10 yards, they have a gully, short cover, mid-off, silly mid-on, short leg, a fine leg and a man on the cover boundary."

French to **Khan, stumped**, the plan worked, it was a slower delivery, teased the batsman to try and go for it, comes down the track and misses it completely. **Quince** makes a great take while jumping up from his crouched position. Lands comfortably and still has plenty of time to whip the bails off whilst the batsman tries to recover his ground. **Quince** knows it is all over and nonchalantly rolls the ball out to the square leg umpire.

Azer Khan	st. Quince b. French	3 off 9 balls	FOW: 221-10

17:02   **Patty @PPringles:** England win the first One Day International of the Jungan Trophy at Lord's!!

CHAPTER 11
ENGLAND 260 ALL OUT.
INDIA 221 ALL OUT.

17:05 "Well that wrapped up quite quickly. England have won the first one day international between England and India, here at the Home of Cricket in North London. In the studio with me to give their thoughts on the day we have former England captains Andy Bird and Jon Knight. In a few minutes we will also be able to go down to Mike who is just getting prepared with the presentation team. First, Ray can you give us the final break down of that Indian batting innings."

"Thanks Patty, India all out for 221 runs in 36.1 overs.

Ravi Kumar, ct. King b. Jules, for 30, India 53 for 1.

Rohan Kumar, st. Quince b. French, for 32, India 71 for 2.

Ankit Bihari, st. Quince b. Chancellor, for 6, India 75 for 3.

S K Trahar, c. French b. Chancellor, for 57, India 176 for 4.

Sunil Sharma, b. Jules, for 52, India 184 for 5.

Nikil Panda, ct. Jones b. Chancellor, for 4, India 186 for 6.

A P Singh, ct. King b. Chancellor, for 3, India 194 for 7.

Shubanka, obstructing the field, for 5, India 203 for 8.

Varun Mopal, ct. Hanson b. French, for 15, India 216 for 9.

Azer Khan, st. Quince b. French, for 3, India 221 all out.

Deepak Pooran not out for 6, Extras 8.

Over to the bowlers,

Mark Jules, 9 overs, no maidens, 59 runs, 2 wickets.

Mohammed Khan, 6 overs, no maidens, 42 runs, no wickets.

Hunter French, 7.1 overs, no maidens, 46 runs, 3 wickets.

Sonia Chancellor, 10 overs, no maidens, 39 runs, 4 wickets.

Patrick Sherman, 4 overs, no maidens, 34 runs, no wickets."

"Thanks Ray, Jon, you first, thoughts on the day?"

"Full credit to England for turning this around. Just over an hour ago they looked dead and buried, Sharma and Trahar were rampant and they should have seen this through to the end. England dug deep, led by Chancellor, got the breakthroughs they needed and got into the tail. It was always going to be difficult for the Indian tail to wag, especially with 50 runs to get. My summary of the day is that it has been riveting. In each period the pendulum swung one way and then back, the boys in the win predictor team must have a headache."

"Andy, you said 'rollercoaster' earlier, that's exactly what it was?"

"I'm exhausted, I can't imagine what the teams are feeling. It was a short game but jam-packed with intrigue and excitement. Let's start right at the beginning of the day. When I was out there with Mike looking at the pitch we both agreed the pitch and the conditions looked like a 300 pitch. England started in that fashion. It wasn't fast scoring by Rhodes and Quince but their partnership set up the team for a good score. Then India came back at them, the spinners in particular. They started taking wickets, making England pay for bad shots and won back the momentum. Jones hung around as long as he could and helped England to something respectable, but it looked low. At halftime we gave lots of credit to the bowling performance and they deserved it. They didn't allow England their full overs allocation. At that point we expected this to be a straightforward chase. 5 an over, bat sensibly and you get there easily. That was reinforced when the Indian openers came out swinging. They took advantage of poor bowling from Jules and Mo. India then lost a few wickets in quick succession, but then we had an hour of play which looked like it was going to finish this game. An excellent 'almost century' stand for the 4th wicket and I had given the game to India. Some of the England fans in the stadium started leaving, or heading out to drown their sorrows. What comes next: massive Indian collapse. 7 wickets for 50 odd runs? That's not good enough at this level and England are the deserved winners. I feel a bit seasick!"

"What about the spinners?"

"They surprised us. This pitch didn't look like a turner. Panda and Shubanka for the Indians, 6 wickets between them, tight bowling and pressure. Then Sonia the same, the only stand-out English bowler. I don't think it was the pitch itself but the attitude that the batsmen had to the spinners. They tried to go after rather than being patient. Both sides are guilty of this. At one point I was thinking that England was short a spinner! That's crazy for Lord's in June."

"Jon what do you say about the quality that was on offer today?"

"I haven't been that impressed, and I think both coaches will be disappointed. Angus will be pleased with the result, but disappointed with the performance. Both teams had chances to take control of this match at different times and close it off. 260 wasn't a great opening score given what we know is in this Lord's pitch. It should have been chased down. Given the result though I have to point most of my disappointment at the Indians. They were in control of this game until 4pm. They had held England to a reasonable, chase-able score, tick. They started strongly, came out of the gates swinging, pressure on the bowlers straight away, tick. Solid middle order partnership to get them within touching distance of it, tick. Then what happened? They lost their heads, they collapsed. They couldn't handle the pressure. Trahar will be angry at himself with the shot, succumbed to the pressure. Sharma got a fantastic ball, unplayable. Panda, Singh are credible batsmen, they let their side down, and that was the game."

17:15   "Thanks gents, with that it is now time for the presentation. Let's head down to Bobby Jungan who will be leading the presentation."

"Good afternoon, everyone, and welcome to the middle after a fantastic day of cricket. I have with me in the presentation party; His Royal Highness the Duke of Exeter, Rajiv Levante, Chairman of the Levante Group, and Priyanka Levante, Global Ambassador for the Levante Group. First we have the prize for the man of the match, as voted for by a panel of journalists and pundits here at Lord's this afternoon, and the winner, for a match winning bowling performance of 10 overs, 4 wickets for 39 runs, is .. Sonia Chancellor. Can I ask Priyanka to present Sonia with a cheque for £5,000 and a bottle of champagne. Sonia can I then ask you to head over there to speak to Mike?"

"Sonia, congratulations on your first Player of the Match for this England side. Are you surprised you got it here at Lord's?"

"Hi Mike, very surprised and quite overwhelmed. Lord's is not normally a good hunting ground for spinners in this format, but what a day we have all had. I tried to follow the example set by Panda and Shubanka, tried to concentrate on my lines, lengths and control, and it worked. I have to give lots of credit to my team too for holding on to the catches! Billy, Sammy, French, and the quick work behind the stumps, they made me look very good today."

"What was it like playing the Indians just after spending so much time with them at the IPL?"

"It was great to see them all again, the Mumbai boys in particular, but they are the enemy here, so we haven't socialised very much. What was useful is that in the IPL we spent a lot of time with the analysts working out how each of these guys like to bat, and more importantly what they don't like! I was able to remember some of those tricks to help me today."

"It seemed you relished bowling at Trahar and Sharma?"

"Sunil I bowled at a lot in the Mumbai nets, but that means he knows a lot of my variations. I have created a few new tricks but he was able to see through them and I wasn't able to get him. Trahar we had a plan for with Mumbai and I just used a similar thinking. He doesn't like to get bogged down, so keeping it tight is important. We had a couple of very close games with Kolkata and he was their main threat. On Kolkata's turning pitch it was my responsibility to get him out! I'm not going to give away all the secrets but yes I have a plan for him. It worked today, tied him up and managed to get him out, which was a bonus."

"You led the bowling comeback, how does it feel to be a leader in this team?"

"We bowl as a team, and we win as a team. That's the mantra coming down from Angus and Billy, and it's what we have all bought into. It was my turn to step up today and do my shift. That's what being part of this team is all about. Mo had a tough day, but the way Jules and Frenchy cleaned up the tail for the win was amazing. We did it as a team. In terms of being a leader, it's a big responsibility for me. I know I am not doing this just for myself but for lots of other girls looking to break into mainstream sports. It's a privileged position to be in and I hope I can do it justice."

"Ready for Friday?"

"Yes these games come back to back, but we are used to that in this short format now. We were playing every other day in India and some of that required flights around the country. Here we just have a short drive up the M1 and then back down here on Sunday. We are one nil up and hopefully we can get all three."

"Thanks Sonia, enjoy this, back to you, Bobby."

"Next we have the losing captain, Sunil Sharma of India, who receives a team bonus cheque of £10,000 from Mr Rajiv Levante, and please then make your way across to Mike for a chat."

"Sunil, commiserations, what went wrong for you today?"

"It's tough to take given where we were and the position we had gotten into. We are not quite sure what went wrong at the moment, it all happened so fast. We did the hard work up front, limited England to a chase-able score, but couldn't convert."

"7 wickets for 45 runs is where it went wrong. What can you say about the English bowling?"

"They did what they needed to. Put the balls in the right place and waited for us to make mistakes. Which we then obliged. They bowled ok, but we were well ahead of the rate early on and were comfortable. Trahar and I were enjoying it out there and we should have finished this off. It's our responsibility as set batsmen to complete the job and we both have broad enough shoulders to accept that. We need to learn and come back stronger."

"What happened there with Shubanka, have you ever seen that before?"

"To be honest I don't want to talk about. Obviously I disagreed with the decision, it didn't look deliberate on the reply, but the umpire made a decision and that was a turning point in the match. It's not worth talking about."

"What positives can you take from today?"

"There are lots, that's why the result is so disappointing. We bowled so well, 260 is not a big score on this ground. I think the average on this ground is well over 300 for both setting and chasing teams. In particular Panda and Shubanka. The spinners stepped up today and the 6 wickets between them is a great result. Panda almost got a 5-for so he should be very proud of todays work, mainly on the bowling side though."

"It seems you aren't too happy with his batting?"

"I think he is disappointed in his shot selection, without going into it anymore. A lot of us will be disappointed this evening. But we have to come back stronger on Friday. This series is still wide open and winnable."

"What do you need to change for Friday?"

"We need some more concentration to get ourselves over the line. We did everything right today but just couldn't finish strong. We will discuss that tonight, then it's closed. These boys are winners, whether in the IPL, Hundred, or for this national team. They don't like losing, especially from a winning position. They will take that anger into Friday and make sure we get over the line. This result will spur us on for the rest of the summer in England."

"Ok, finally, a question from one of our twitter followers, you just got your cheque from Mr. Rajiv Levante, Priyanka's father, I guess you know him quite well, have you had any specific conversations with him recently?"

"I can't say I have any idea what you mean Mike! Haha."

"Thanks Sunil, unlucky today and see you again on Friday. Back to you, Bobby."

17:30   "Finally, can I welcome the winning captain, William Jones, to come and receive the winning bonus cheque of £20,000 from His Royal Highness the Duke of Exeter and to also then make his way across to have a chat with Mike. Congratulations to William and England for a great performance today and for the win."

"Congratulations, Billy great performance today, how did you turn that around?"

"All the congratulations should go straight to the bowlers to be honest, they somehow pulled us out of a big hole. Rabbit from a hat type of performance, we are very proud of them tonight."

"260 was enough it seems?"

"Haha, I told you it would be enough! Trust me mate! No, no obviously we were concerned, and we were not happy with our batting. Too many errant shots. We had a solid base though couldn't convert it. Quince and I had starts, got to 50 but couldn't push on from there and get a big score. We had targeted 320 at the start of the day so to only come home with 260 is disappointing. But like I said credit to the bowling unit for making it look like a great score."

"How do you turn the batting around for the rest of the series?"

"We have to keep doing what we are doing. Try and keep our heads in the game and commit for the full 50 overs. We have the talent to put up a big score and we need to show everyone, and ourselves, that we can do it."

"Let's come back to the second innings. You give the bowlers lots of credit but it didn't start too well, Kumar, Kapoor, Sharma and Trahar all made runs?"

"Yeah we didn't start well. When you spend the first 10 overs chasing the ball all over the ground you get tired and your shoulders drop. You feel the pressure. That's where we need to improve, have to keep the positive attitude to keep ploughing on. All of the quickies took a beating from those four. They are top quality batsmen, all in form, coming off a big IPL season where they all scored runs, I am not surprised. We have bowling plans for all of them and we will have to do better to contain next time."

"And then you turned it around out of nowhere?"

Sonia stepped up and I am glad someone did. We had seen how effective the spinners were in the morning, how much trouble they gave us, and Sonia fed off that to give us a match winning performance. 4 for 30 something? Against this quality of batsmen on a flat Lord's pitch, it's a fantastic performance. I would put her on Lords' boards if I could. In terms of how it changed the game it was more valuable than a 5-for. When we had new batsmen at the crease and some runs left on the board we got an energy boost. We were running in harder, backing up better, and our world class attack showed who they are."

"Did King redeem himself with those catches? Will he get a slot on Friday?"

"He doesn't need to redeem himself. We bat as a team and we scored 260 as a team. Whether you score 1 or 100 in that it doesn't matter. He's a newbie so gets stuck in at short leg as a rite of passage and made it count today. I don't think my reactions are quick enough to cover that ground and take those sorts of catches anymore! For Friday we are not going to make any decisions at the moment. We will analyse today's performance, in particular, what worked well and what didn't, and then make a decision on Friday morning based on the conditions in Birmingham. We have a great squad to pick from, they all deserve a place and we will pick a team to go for the win."

"You did take a good one too, don't forget! Thanks William, and congratulations again, see you on Friday. With that we are done down here, Patty, back to you in the Studio."

"Thanks Mike, we will see you on Friday too. Jon final thoughts of the day?"

"Well let me say that I agree with the player of the match choice. I voted for her as she has stepped up and turned this game around for England. She had a massive impact on it both in terms of the pressure she applied and the wickets she took. So congrats to her. Neither side were at their best and they will acknowledge that. They have to improve for the rest of the series, but I expect them all to do that. It is early in the summer and plenty of cricket still to come."

"Andy, favourite moment of the game for you?"

"Funniest moment was when Jules almost got attacked by those pigeons. I guess he will learn to not shout so loud next time. Strangest moments either when King walked on to his own stumps or when Shubanka got given from obstructing play. Each side got one strange thing, so I guess that's fair at least. My favourite moment must be the most impactful and that was Sonia's 8th over, when she stifled Trahar and got his wicket. Until that point it was India's to lose. The game turned at that point and sparked the collapse. I know our listeners actually missed that over because of the shipping forecast but perhaps that will be lucky in the future! We should just replace the entire broadcast with what is happening in the North Sea and England will win all their matches!?"

Thanks for that Andy, Jon, appreciate your time with me today in the studio. It has been a great cricketing adventure, and we look forward to following it up with more action later this week. To remind everyone we will be broadcasting live from Edgbaston from 9am on Friday morning and the final One-Day match of the series is on Sunday, back in London at the Oval. For the time being England take a 1-nil lead in the Jungan Trophy and we will see you all on Friday. Good Evening."

THE MATCH LETTERS

England's Innings:

thatwomanappearedoutofnowhereafewyardsapartinthenarrowmoo

nlitlaneforasecdykthihehadeverseenandhehadseensomeexremelyod

dthingshewatcohweallkpresentsoutofhisarmsasthethreeofthemhead

edbwashisfavouritebthe*heirraggedbthattherewasatenthousandgall

eonpricewhenydrac

India's Innings:

Widedrivewaythatledoffthelanethehighhedgechehadthoughthekhe

stialookhagriddothedragonfirethingagainletsgetoutofhereholdontig

htthenharrytherewasadeafenw*nhisscteatdumbhecsilentandwatcda

ysoldnewskshegraspedsodramaticspellswork

* = Pigeon effect

THE KAMDAR FOUNDATION

The MC & KM Kamdar Foundation (registered UK charity number: 1153329) is a family charity trust that promotes the advancement of health and education, relief of poverty and other charitable purposes within the United Kingdom and other countries throughout the world specifically Kenya (where our family roots are), Uganda, Rwanda, India, South America etc.. The Foundation is committed to providing relief for those in need, by reason of youth, age, ill-health, disability, financial hardship or any other disadvantage.

Within the United Kingdom, the Foundation has supported a number of charities e.g. World Cancer Research Fund, Macmillan Cancer Support, St. Luke's Hospice, RNIB, MYTON Hospice, Cancer Research UK, Shishukunj, Diabetes UK, CDLS Foundation, Food 4 life, Kings College Hospital, BAPS Charities, Sightsavers, British Heart Foundation, Young Indian Vegetarians, Southall Black Sisters, Concern Worldwide, Mencap, Alzheimer's Society.

In the rest of the world, the Foundation has worked with and supported a range of good causes e.g. NVA (Jiv Daya India), Jain Social Group (Kenya cataract operations), AVDBF (India schools for the blind and mental asylums), BEHT (India schools), Shree Jalaram (Kenya chemotherapy treatments), Action Aid (Kenya), The Kniamam Project (Rwanda), Rotary Club (India dialysis machines), Literacy India Project (India), Raj Saubhag Satsang (India)
I am pleased that with his book I will be able to make a contribution to the noble work that my family's Foundation does.

EPILOGUE

How did the game play out, what would I do differently next time, and what was my experience like?

The game was always going to be a risk. I warned you at the beginning. In my testing when I ran the games I was achieving scores of around 300. Ok it is very different to the 400+ scores we get in real life, though there was a competitive base level. At least that gave me a point of reference to be able to say that 260 seemed low. In today's game it is very low. The IPL and other big bash tournaments have geared the game towards clearing the fences and entertaining the crowds. This scoring system did not set up well for that. There was only one 6 (f) and one 4 (g) option, and they don't come up that often. I was expecting 300+ and that made 260 an interesting score. Further it seemed that it was a very low score when the chasing team was sitting on 176-3 after 25 overs. That's a 400+ run rate in the real world and so 260 shouldn't have been any problem. Then the collapse came – and it played out very differently. Of course, this can happen in the real world too, but 7 for 45 runs is very unusual, especially on the flat one-day pitches that we see today.

The "wicket" deliveries just kept coming back to back. But until the final ball India still had a chance to win it. This format is a bit agnostic in terms of quality position and time at the crease. So apart from a few changes in the scoring system, a few letters different, it treats a settled number 4 the same as a new number 11. This format allows for a 100-run 10th wicket partnership. We didn't get that, which is realistic, but on another day perhaps we could have. We would have only needed another 40 runs for a different result, which at the scoring rate this game was providing could have been 5 or 6 overs. But it gave the entertainment that we expect from live action. Yo-yo changes, momentum changes, ups and downs, no idea who is going to win until the end. I liked that because we all enjoy watching cricket and we normally know what to expect in any situation. We have all sat watching a game which felt like it was over, even if it was only halfway done. A team scores 200 in an ODI, we give the game to the chasers, even more so if they start 100-0. A team scores 400 on a 250 pitch, and the chasers have no chance. This game swung wildly both ways as it was being played out. The game surprised me, just like the real world.

I will now own up: I made some mistakes. Those tracking me against the actual book will have realised this already. Did it affect the game? Some yes some no. It turned out that playing this over such a long period of time meant that my scoring skills were not very good. The small stuff first, you will have noticed that there were many extra ball wides missed. I was able to add some story after the fact, though couldn't go back and change the game after it had played out. The big thing, I missed one whole over! The 35th over in the England innings. 34 became 36. This is a problem in this game. At the next wicket we moved to a new page that was decided by which over we were on. 40 vs 41 is a different page, a different story line, a completely different score. To confirm the second innings wasn't affected by this as we started again on page 2. I apologise for this but the only solace I take is that England were 225 for 7 at the time of the mistake. Given that India only got to 221, it wouldn't have changed the result. Perhaps we would have gotten another 10 overs of England batting, and perhaps a 300+ first innings score? I won't go back and check it as there are no "take backs" in live sport!

Overall that was a long and difficult experiment. We have been lockdown for the last 8 months in the UK with not much else to do, but still it was tough to get the game played and the words down on the page. For me, and, I presume, other amateur writers, the energy to keep going came in batches. There were times when I was on it, wanted to keep going, wanted to push the story forward, and there were other times when I forgot about it completely. There is a sense of accomplishment with finishing though and counting up the words and finding that we got close to 70 thousand! Now that I am finished, I loved the experience and the accomplishment. Whether we get a day 2 of the series will depend on your desire to read another, given that you can't read this one again!

Printed in Great Britain
by Amazon